Ananas comosus variegatus
The variegated pineapple

BROMELIADS IN COLOR

AND THEIR CULTURE

A COMPILATION

FROM THE BULLETINS

of

THE BROMELIAD SOCIETY

by

VICTORIA PADILLA
EDITOR

1966

FOREWORD

When the Bromeliad Society was organized in 1950, little had been written about the family of plants known as the Bromeliaceae. True, there were the botannical studies of Lyman B. Smith and the delightful travel adventure *Brazil, Orchid of the Tropics* by Mulford and Racine Foster, but there was nothing to aid the plantsman in his culture of bromeliads. The Society bulletins, first issued in 1951, and the cultural handbook, published in 1953, were the first works in English to be devoted in their entirety to the culture of these plants. That these publications have been highly successful is evidenced by the rapid growth of the Society and the world-wide interest now shown in bromeliads.

From the very first, the articles which have appeared in the bulletins have been of outstanding merit, and there has been a continuous demand for back issues, which unfortunately are no longer available. For this reason, the Society has deemed it expedient to reprint the articles that evoked special interest or seemed of particular value to the amateur. Although some of the articles date back over a decade, their material is as fresh and up to date as if written today. The only changes that should be made are those pertaining to nomenclature: *Aechmea marmorata* is now *Quesnelia marmorata, Ananas ananasoides* var. *nana* is now *Ananas nanus,* and *Dyckia sulphurea* has become *Dyckia brevifolia.* A new genus Fosterella has been added in the Pitcairnoideae sub-family.

The Society is indebted to Jack O. Holmes, Ed Hummel, The Bromeliad Society of Louisiana, the Bromeliad Society of La Ballona Valley, and the Bromeliad Guild of Los Angeles for helping to get this book "off the ground." Special thanks go to Mulford B. Foster for his editorial help and to the following for the use of their kodachromes: David Barry, Jr., Ralph Cornell, Hattie Davidson, Dr. William F. Dunbar, Charles Ferveda, Mulford B. Foster, Charles Hodgson, Jack Holmes, Ed Hummel, Marcel Lecoufle, Elmer Lenz, Jules Padilla, Ralph Spenser, and Charles Wiley.

Victoria Padilla

Los Angeles, California
January, 1966.

CONTENTS

CULTURE

PROPAGATION

DISPLAY

WHY BROMELIAD?

Lyman B. Smith

Obviously "Bromeliad" is simply a shortening of the scientific name "Bromeliaceae" to indicate any member of the Pineapple family. We might call them all pineapples since they are members of that family, and not bother to find a new term. However, it would cause confusion to associate such diverse forms as the giant Puya and the Spanish moss under a name for which we have already a sharp and narrow concept. As the Bromeliaceae were unknown before the discovery of America, we did not have any such ancient general term for the family as there was in the case of grasses, sedges, lilies or orchids, and one had to be manufactured.

It is not possible to say now who first coined the word "Bromeliad" but it was probably some fairly recent botanist or horticulturist who was tired of having to use the phrase "species of Bromeliaceae" after the cumbrous and stately fashion of the old school. French and German botanists of the nineteenth century regularly used such single words for members of one family, had a standard way of making them, and seemed to find nothing undignified in the process.

The second step in tracing our genealogy is to find the origin of "Bromeliaceae" and this is very clear. With few exceptions the scientific name of a plant family is derived by combining the name of one of its genera with the ending "aceae." Thus in 1805 the French botanist, Jaume Saint-Hilaire, defined the Bromeliaceae and formed the family name from the genus Bromelia.

Our next step takes us back to Linnaeus the father of systematic botany for he it was who established the genus Bromelia in 1754 according to the rules we now follow in making scientific names. The name was taken from the family name of Olof Bromelius, a Swedish botanist. Since Linnaeus also was Swedish, we might at first suppose that he had named the genus for a friend, but Bromelius died before Linnaeus was born.

Actually it was Plumier, the early French explorer of the West Indies, who first had the idea of renaming for Mr. Bromelius the genus that previously had gone by the Indian name of Karatas, and Linnaeus so credited it. Plumier was on familiar terms with the genus Bromelia in the West Indies. Bromelius, on the other hand, was famous mainly for the fine Flora that he wrote for his home town of Goetheborg and it is by no means certain that he ever laid eyes on a single plant of the great group that was to bear his name.

Associate Curator, Div. Phanerogams, Smithsonian Institution.

❊   ❊   ❊

A few years ago, in a conversation with Dr. Lyman B. Smith, the matter of a common or nick-name for bromeliad came up. It was his feeling that we should agree, if possible, on the use of *one* common name. After considering them all he thought that if the word bromeliad was to have a more simple form it should be "bromel." As the family was named for Bromelius, so the word bromel seemed the most apropos as the abbreviated form.   M.B.F.

BROMELIADS — GEOGRAPHICAL DISTRIBUTION

Walter Richter

One peculiarity of this family is its limited distribution. All bromeliads are natives of the Americas. Their occurence is, of course, limited by climatic conditions — temperature being probably the main factor, and light and humidity to a certain extent being another cause. Humidity is especially important to the epiphytic species that cannot survive prolonged periods of dryness. Only a few species have managed to adapt themselves to drought and cold and have been able, due to their resistance to adversity, to penetrate regions where winters are felt.

Tillandsia usneoides, with astonishing adaptibility, has spread most widely. Mez called it the character plant of the tropical Americas, being known from Florida to northern Chile and Central Argentine. The territorial limits of the distribution, according to Harms, is from 38° north in eastern Virginia to 44° south in Chile. It is doubtful whether bromeliads can exist beyond these limits. The genus Tillandsia contains the most adverse — tolerant species — and are the pioneers of the tribe. We can only form a vague conception of the various growing conditions existing in such a vast area.

One might say it is unnecessary for the practical grower to concern himself with all this and that a mere knowledge of simple cultural requirements is all that is needed to grow bromels profitably. To attain a fair success in growing bromeliads it is not absolutely necessary that the practical grower know everything pertaining to them; but to reach perfection, this knowledge of their peculiarities, demands, and preferences should be his.

Location, situation, and climate form the plant. By looking at a plant, noting its appearance and condition, the experienced grower can usually tell with some certainty its cultural needs. A study of their natural growing conditions — of where they grow and their situation — indicates the rudiments of cultural requirements of bromeliads to a greater degree than with any other plant group. These natural growing conditions are very diversified, depending upon available light, wind, temperature, the form and amount of atmospheric precipitation — be it rain, fog, or dew — the form, size, color, and structure of the leaves and the density of the scale covering are to the largest degree expressive of the climatic conditions.

The above indicated enormous area — its north and south extent limited by temperature, and its east and west borders by two oceans and maritime currents, and, finally, by the temperature affected by altitude — fosters an amazing variety of forms, which often grow in such large masses as to give the landscape an aspect of its own. Every district has its typical representatives, which are some-times widespread and which are sometimes limited regionally.

Many species are inhabitants of the tropical rain forests. These forests cover, for the most part, the vast expanses of the lower Amazon basin and are the concept of "the forest primeval." The larger part of this forest is water-covered during March and April, twice yearly in the lower regions when the rivers reach flood stages. So bromeliads have taken to the trees, and here grow most of the epiphytic species. The rain forests of Brazil, influenced climatically, vary region-ally very much. They shelter an enormous number of species and forms. A great many of the horticulturally valuable Vriesias have their home there. They are not too heat demanding, a part of the territory being outside the tropical belt. To know this is of special importance to the grower. The main forms of the rain-forest bromels are the soft-leaved leaf-tank types, unarmed and without scales. The greater number have magnificently colored inflorescences. Their light requirements are comparatively low, situated as they are below shading leaf-crowns and foliage masses.

Bromels inhabiting the Catinga region, with its limited rainfall and thorny bush growth, have contrastingly stiff, well-armored leaves. Aechmeas, Ananas, Bromélia species, and others grow there. These plants are pronounced sun lovers, are very drought-resistant, and are, for the most part, terrestrials. These character qualities should be well considered by the grower.

The third group to be considered is that of the Savannas, a park-like land-scape with extensive grassy plains, small tree groups, and large single trees. Their temperature is that of the rain-forests, but the strong prevailing wind exercises a major influence and the humidity is subject to great variation. All bromels native in this region are either epiphytic or grow upon isolated rock formations. All are very drought resistant and are able to regulate their water intake by various means; for instance, by a specially dense scale covering or by large capacious leaves. The grower must consider that these bromeliads are often exposed to strong light, the trees being less dense and often deciduous.

All these various regions intergraded, are more or less pronounced, inhabited often by special forms not mentioned here. These climatically conditioned zones reappear in more condensed form in Central America, inhabited by similarly influenced forms of vegetation. The epiphytic species are best able to overcome the manifold adverse conditions and are represented in greatest numbers. Eleva- . tion forms a growth limit at about 12,000 feet in the South American Andes of Peru, Brazil, and Argentina. There Puyas are predominant, attaining often a gigantic size.

Again and again it should be realized that growth regions are seldom sharply

3

defined. They are fluent, and transition zones are numerous, influencing growth and forms and presupposing an adaptability within wide limits. This is indeed the case. The total effect of these climatic factors with narrow limits has produced conditions for existence that have formed highly selective species among the bromeliads and strictly limited their occurrence to restricted zones. This explains in part the difficulties sometime met with in their cultivation, their failure to do their best if individual needs are disregarded, neglected — due chiefly to lack of knowledge.

Summary

I. Ever humid regions — rain forests.
More or less dense shade, unvarying high temperature, light air movement.

II. Tropical regions with pronounced dry periods.

    a. Chapparal-like regions, covered with thorny bushes.

    b. Savannas.

Strong to very strong light, more or less dry spells. Considerable variation in humidity, periodical moderate temperature variation, moderate to dry high temperatures, frequent strong air movements, with low temperatures occuring in the savannas.

Bringing Bromeliads from the Amazon jungle

INTRODUCTION INTO CULTIVATION

Excerpt from Walter Richter's *Bromeliad Handbook*
"Anzucht und Kultur der Bromeliaceen" (1950)
Translated by Joseph Schneider

European growers showed interest in bromeliads at a comparatively early date. Their beauty, their oddity and mainly, the tenacity with which they cling to life, are probably the chief reasons for their early appearance into cultivation. They endured the long sea voyagees of that time which other plant material could not survive. That two of the toughest-leaved species were the first to arrive in Europe seems to prove this assertion. These were, according to Altons in "Hortus Kewensis" the species *Bromelia ananas* (synonym for *Ananas comosus*) and *Bromelia pinguin,* the year of introduction being 1690. In 1776 they were followed by *Caraguata lingulata* [genus now known as Guzmania]. In 1811 the famous Kew Gardens had already sixteen species; in 1864 that number had mounted to one hundred, and after acquisition of the very large collection of the Morrens in 1887 the total rose to 252 species.

The Botanical Garden of the Dutch University at Leyden, under the direction of Inspector Wittes, who had a considerable knowledge of bromeliads, listed in 1894, the large number of 334 species.

The widely known and well liked *Vriesia splendens* was introduced from the Guianas in 1842 and 1844 by Melinon and Leperieur. At about the same time *Aechmea fulgens* came from Brazil; a little later, September 1846, *Aechmea fasciata* flowered for the first time at the establishment of Van Houtte in Ghent.

The magnificent winter-flowering *Guzmania musaica* was discovered in December, 1867. The collector, G. Wallis, found it in a dense forest near Teoroma, near Ocana, New Granada [Colombia] in the drainage basin of the Magdalena River, and sent it to Europe.

In 1872 J. Linden, of Belgium, received *Vriesia tesselata* from Brazil and it flowered for the first time ten years later. *Vriesia hieroglyphica* proved very difficult to bring to flower; it was successfully accomplished in 1880. During the first half of the nineteenth century many Billbergia species were brought in. Their durability and toleration of adverse conditions probably favored their introduction.

The history of the introduction of bromeliads is interesting; the few dates mentioned show it to have concurred with that gala period which brought so many orchids and other beautiful tropicals in great quantities to Europe. Not only nurseries, but many private collectors and plant-friends took a great interest in them. Through their efforts expeditions were financed and organized and collectors sent out who, at times, risked their lives in the search for new, rare and precious plant material.

The Belgians played a main role, and many of their names are forever remembered in scientific annals and garden literature. Jean Linden, himself, traveled through middle and South America from 1835 to 1845, and after establishing his own firm in Brussels, sent out collectors. His new introductions made his name famous; thanks to his initiative, about 1100 orchid species and 1500 other plants, among them many bromeliads, came to Europe; Roezl, Schliem, Libon, Wallis, Giesbrecht [probably means A. B. Ghiesbreght, Belgian collector] and others, collected for him. Many plants, well known horticulturally, bear their names.

Belgian gardeners, like DeJonghe-Brussel, Louis van Houtte, of Ghent, Alexander Verschaffelt, Charles van Eckhoute, and others too, contributed materially to the introduction of bromeliads. Thus, naturally, the greatest collections were established in Belgium, notably the one of Jacob-Makoy in Liege. The Botanical Garden in Liege had the largest collection in the eighties of the past century; at that time it was under the directorship of one of the foremost authorities on bromeliads, i.e. Professor Charles Morren.

Vriesea splendens

The French garden architect, Edouard Andre, maintained a large collection; he collected himself, and later, sent out other collectors.

The Frenchman, Charles Pinel, formerly a merchant in Brazil, and Morel at St. Mande, near Paris, were great enthusiasts; plants bearing their names give testimony, and honor their efforts. Marius Porte, mainly active in the Philippines, introduced some bromeliads, such as *Billbergia porteana,* and others.

In Germany, little of consequence was done, neither in discovering new species nor in their introduction, but botanical gardens and private estates started and kept large collections; this helped much to create and spread interest in bromeliads.

At about the turn of the century, the interest in these beautiful and fascinating plants slackened considerably, other matters gained preponderance. World War I flamed across Europe and destroyed nearly all that was still left. After the effect of the inflation period wore off, the changing tasks gradually reawakened the interest in special plants and revived the interest in bromeliads in the mid-thirties. It had barely begun when the second World War broke off the budding development. I am convinced the future is bright for bromeliads. The enrichment of the present assortment, will further the interest and re-establish their growing and sale. These plants surely merit it.

6

BLUEPRINT OF THE JUNGLE

Mulford B. Foster

Journal of the New York Botanical Garden, January, 1945
Reprinted by Permission

For hours we had been cutting our way through a dry, brambly jungle out in Mato Grosso and at last we had found a haven for rest. Suddenly, we looked up into the forest "penthouse" above us. A rustle of leaves and vigorous swaying of branches focused our attention on a spry Capuchin monkey; something was wrong in his world! Without asking, we had intruded into his domain, had entered his dining-room to eat our lunch. He wasn't too certain what to do about it. He leaped down three flights, from "floor to floor" of his jungle home to investigate these visitors more thoroughly. As we watched him we were reminded, as we had been many times before, of the structural character of the Brazilian jungle. While the jungle forests seem endlessly varied, always they seem patterned or blueprinted in the form of a great building with one, two, three, or even four "stories" of growth.

In the great Cerrado or Cantinga (scrub lands) only the first floor of vegetation occurs, but in the great primeval forests in various mountain ranges, such as the Serra das Aymores, the Serra do Mar, or the Serra da Mantigueira, we always observ-ed three or four distinct stories, with even a "penthouse" above. The strata of plant growth are more or less comparable to strata of rock formation, and it is singular-ly interesting to note how strictly the plants which grow in the trees keep to their own strata. Seldom do you find a given plant growing in more than one of these areas.

The ground floor of course is always more easily observed than any of the others. For the most part the plants on the first floor of the big forest are lush, the leaves are broad, of more tender and rapid growth, and the plants are naturally shade-loving. They are likely to be a tangled mass of ferns, calatheas, tradescantias, heliconias, pipers or bromeliads. As I am especially interested in the bromeliads, I am naturally more aware of the strata in which these particular plants grow, though they follow a pat-tern of habitat similar to that of other epiphytic forms such as orchids, cacti, ferns, and pipers. In fact, my own blueprint of the jungle growth is based mainly on the habitats of bromeliads.

Neoregelia, Nidularium and Canistrum are three bromeliaceous genera which can be found on the first floor of growth, since they like the moisture and shade of the lowest parts. Seldom do they ever venture high above the ground, but actually the ground is often so crowded with verdant growth of other plants that they do seek the low trunks, stumps, or low-slung lianas. And strangely, the vegetative growth of these particular bromeliads is more luxuriant and showy, while the flowers and fruits of these plants are less spectacular than on those that grow higher up. The conditions in the shadows of the rain forests make these plants well adaptable for corners and neglected places of the greenhouse or conservatory and shaded parts of a home. I generally place most of my Nidulariums, Canistrums or Neoregelias under slat benches or under other foliage plants in my greenhouse for they are much less inclined to grow out of form and shape than plants which strive harder to reach the light.

The ground floor in the jungle, of course, acts also as a starting point or foot-hold for climbing plants which sometimes go on up to the roof. Although many of the luxuriantly growing plants of the first floor covering have the ability to out-grow and overshadow other growth in almost complete shade, in horticultural use they generally are less adaptable to sudden changes in temperature and light than those in the upper strata. These first floor plants of the jungle, such as Nidulariums, calatheas, ferns, and others, require, as a rule, more constant conditions. On the other hand, some of the plants, like the aroids and other climbers which have their feet on the first floor, adjust themselves to various levels. They defy any of the other growth to outdo them, so they get off the ground and take to the spaciousness of the trees. Thus, because of this resourcefulness to rise above their conditions, they often become more adaptable under artificial conditions as house plants. They are prepared in nature for a transition to the cave-dweller conditions of a home. So, we continuously search for plants that can stand shade and the heated room, and that have the ability to stay with people whom it is often difficult to understand.

In many jungles the foliage of the cacaos and other low-branched trees makes the roof covering of the first floor. In practically every jungle area in Brazil the willowy cecropias serve as the roof of the first and second story of the growth. They are usually on the edge of the dense jungle and seem to act as nurses who stand in readiness to protect the tender growth below them, should anything happen to the dense, high "roof" proper. The great, broad palmate leaves of these rapidly growing cecropias protect the young seedlings of other plants until they are able to take care of themselves.

Among the bromeliads, species of Billbergia, Vriesia, many of Aechmea and some of Tillandsia have taken residence on the second floor. Occasionally a Quesnelia, Hohenbergia or a Streptocalyx also may have chosen this area. These plants are a bit more independent of moist conditions and enjoy more light than their first floor cousins. Consequently, they are inclined to be more showy in form and flower. The tree-tops of this level are more open and enough light filters through to create a situation that will harbor plants, especially bromeliads, which are favorable to greenhouse, sunporch or patio conditions. They do not need quite so much moist atmosphere or diligent attention as those growing lower down.

Here in the more open second floor we find many of the climbing and vine-like palms, and the tree-like species of Opuntia. These cacti which stand with their feet in the acid-leaf-mold and enjoy the forest shade are only just beginning, in the course of their evolution, to show the typical succulent pads of their desert relatives.

The layman thinks of cacti as being almost exclusively residents of the desert, and while this may be more or less true in Mexico and our Southwest, it is not entirely so in Brazil. South American jungles must have been the original home of that great family for we still find a predominance of the earlier leafy forms of cacti there. Rhipsalis, Hatiora, Zygocactus, and other genera of epiphytic cacti abound in most jungle areas of Brazil, being habitues of the second floor along with Aechmea, Billbergia and Vriesia of the bromeliads. The well-known Zygocactus (Christmas cactus) grows happily on the first and second floor in the moist shade of the coolest jungles.

On the third floor of any given Brazilian jungle, will be found a predominance of Aechmea, a stiffer and sterner type of bromeliad which is seeking more light and more air currents. Of course, Vriesia and Tillandsia will be found here, also, on the "mezzanine" between second and third floor, as it were, made up of the lower limbs of the giant trees whose leaf heads form the roof and penthouse areas above.

Some of our most interesting discoveries were found in this third floor stratum, the structure of which is made up of great limbs of the towering forest trees which throw out their far-reaching branches, filtering the light for trees and vegetation below. Here in these giant trees we find giant bromeliads; in size some of them are so immense that one wonders why they have not taken to the ground instead. It was in southern Bahia in a primeval forest back from Ilheos, when we discovered the two new species, *Aechmea conifera* and *Aechmea depressa,* that we had our first experience in seeing really giant plants completely at ease fastened securely in their high, lofty positions on limbs almost as large as ordinary trees, 80 feet up from the ground. The trees in which they live are often eight to ten feet in diameter. To reach these air plants we had to do as the monkey does. First we climbed into the trees of the first and second floors, their branches intermeshed with the taller trees of the second and third floors. From limb to limb with the help of great swinging vines we finally reached the third floor, or the lower branches of the largest trees. It is no easy job; in fact, sometimes it takes from one to two hours to successfully reach those plants and loosen them from their secure quarters. Lowering them with ropes and bringing them to earth, we finally realized their immense size. *Aechmea conifera* had a cone-like flower head which, when fully developed, was eighteen inches long and weighed twelve pounds. One of these plants with its several side shoots and its partly cast off previous growth may weigh 100 to 125 pounds. And right in this one mass of plant life there is plenty of interest in other forms of life for the ranologist, herpetologist, entomologist, and botanist, because frogs, snakes, and beetles, as well as aquatic mosses and algae, make up the great variety of life in the little universe in the series of pools within the leaf cups of one great epiphyte. These giant air plants, in spite of the animals and the one or two gallons of water they hold, hang on securely with their wire-like roots in a perfect balancing act.

The character of the fourth story is more open and thereby more sparsely inhabited by bromeliads. The higher the area the stiffer and more rugged the bromeliad. If the plant holds water in its basal leaf-cups, the leaves may have more spines; but if the plants (like the xerophytic tillandsias) do not hold water between their leaves, then their bodies will be covered with countless peltate scales. These scales serve both as an insulation against sun and wind and act also as sponge cups to soak up moisture from the cool, dewy air. Naturally these higher stratum air plants are the most independent of all the plants. That is, they are independent of what we generally term as favorable conditions. As house plants they are, however, quite, susceptible to excessive coddling, often succumbing quickly to too much moisture, for they have developed their xerophytic qualities on a parallel with desert dewellers and cannot stand a "soft" life. For example, *Tillandsia recurvata* (ball moss), has become so conditioned and hardened that it could be called a xerophytic or saxicolous plant as well as an epiphytic one, finding lodging on desert cacti or among rocks quite as comfortably as on trees in temperate or tropical zones. This Tillandsia has probably the greatest adaptability of any plant in the Western Hemisphere.

Many of the tropical plants, especially those growing at some elevation in the mountains are what we would call coolhouse plants, for at home they have heat only in the middle of the day. I often wish that more growers, especially those who are confined to greenhouses in the north, could personally experience these jungles and feel the many conditions under which the plants live. And, since many of the epiphytes love cool nights, they seem quite remarkable in their adaptability to withstand the hothouse treatment day and night that they receive when confined far from their native arboreal air gardens. They like more air than we are inclined to give them, and more variation in temperature. Plants which are fastened in one position through their life must have plenty of exercise.

How can a plant have exercise? By raising and lowering of temperature, by alternating drying out and watering periods; these changes, mixed with good, pure ventilation will keep a plant active and in vigorous health. There are often conditions even in the forest which are detrimental to some of the plants some of the time. The vitality of certain ones is lowered and we find scale and other insects there, but where the plants have the proper exercise and ventilation with their natural source of food you find them endowed with a much greater resistance and fewer insect enemies that you find when they are confined in a glasshouse.

Unfortunately, bromeliads and orchids as greenhouse or house plants cannot always get the rain water which means so much to them and often must get along on chemically treated water which has the very life taken out of it. That many of them hold up remarkably well under this deficiency in their diet demands our great admiration. One caution is important: bromeliads and orchids cannot thrive very long with excessively alkaline water.

I believe also that epiphytic plants in the greenhouse should have the association of other kinds of plant growth around them. Human beings cannot live without plants, neither can plants live without other plants, but we are quite sure that plants can live without human beings. Little do we know of the beneficial gaseous atmosphere that is given out by the various plants. Some plants may give off ethylene (a gas in wood smoke) which has been proved to have an action on bromeliads in that it forces them to bloom out of season. What gases are given off and what their resultant actions are present a vast field for investigation.

When one thoughtfully surveys the different stories of the jungle growth, its inhabitants, and its living conditions from the perspective of the first "floor" one realizes that the great mass of epiphytic life clinging to the trunks and overhanging branches forms a garden quite removed from the earth, a garden "in suspension."

The successive strata or stories of vegetation, in which different types of epiphytic plants make their homes give the jungle its blueprint, or pattern.

Rt. 3. Box 658, Orlando, Florida.

THE SUBFAMILIES AND GENERA OF THE BROMELIACEAE[1]

Lyman B. Smith

1. Seeds variously appendaged (naked in *Navia*, but the ovary superior and the fruit dehiscent); ovary wholly or in part superior (wholly inferior in *Pitcairnia anomala*); fruit a capsule (but indehiscent in a few species of *Pitcairnia*).
   2. Seeds with entire appendages, not plumose; ovary usually wholly or in part superior; leaves often spinose-serrate; plants almost always terrestrial.
      Subfamily 1. *Pitcairnioideae*.
   2. Seeds plumose; ovary nearly or quite superior (except in *Glomeropitcairnia*); leaves always entire; plants chiefly epiphytic............................ Subfamily 2. *Tillandsioideae*.
1. Seeds always naked; ovary wholly or in very large part (*Acanthostachys*) inferior; fruit always baccate, fleshy to coriaceous; leaves usually spinose-serrate; plants often epiphytic..Subfamily 3. *Bromelioideae*.

Subfamily 1. Pitcairnioideae
1. Seeds appendaged; sepals convolute with the left side of each overlapping the right of the next one.
   2. Petals free; filaments not forming a tube.
      3. Flowers perfect.
         4. Ovary wholly superior.
            5. Petals naked.
               6. Seeds broad, with a wing surrounding at least three sides; plants usually large and coarse.
                  7. Petals broad, much more conspicuous than the sepals, strongly spirally twisted together after anthesis; seed-wing little if at all produced ......*Puya*.
                  7. Petals narrow, inconspicuous; seed-wing produced dorsally...... *Encholirium*.
               6. Seeds narrow, caudate-appendaged or apiculate at each pole; petals not twisted together after anthesis.
                  8. Seeds or ovules merely apiculate; placentae basal.................*Cottendorfia*.
                  8. Seeds long-caudate; placentae usually extending almost the height of the cell.
                     9. Petals white, separate after anthesis; sepals not over 5 mm. long, thin, flat; plants slender..*Lindmania*.
                     9. Petals brightly colored, more or less massed together after anthesis but not twisted; sepals larger and firmer; plants relatively robust.........*Connellia*.
            5. Petals each bearing a single large scale near the base.
               10. Spreading shrubs; the scape with a definite cambium layer; inflorescence paniculate...*Deuterocohnia*.
               10. Low cushion-forming plants; scape lacking; inflorescences one-flowered, at the ends of the branches. (Including *Meziothamnus*).........*Abromeitiella*.
         4. Ovary at least partly inferior.
            11. Flowers large and conspicuous, usually zygomorphic; petals often appendaged, several times as long as the ovary; ovules numerous ....*Pitcairnia*.
            11. Flowers minute, regular; petals naked, usually shorter than the ovary; ovules few.
               Brocchinia.
      3. Flowers functionally unisexual with one sex aborted, inconspicuous, never more than 15 mm. long; ovary from wholly superior to very slightly so. (Including *Bakerantha*).
         Hechtia.
   2. Petals joined centrally to a tube formed by the bases of the filaments but their margins free, yellow or orange; seeds winged. (Including *Prionophyllum*).................*Dyckia*.
1. Seeds naked; sepals imbricate with both posterior ones overlapping the anterior...........*Navia*

----
[1]Revised from "Plant Life" 1: 40-44. 1945. Published by permission of the Secretary of the Smithsonian Institution.

Subfamily 2. Tillandsioideae.

1. Ovary wholly or almost wholly superior.
   2. Appendage of the seed basal, straight at maturity.
      3. Petals free or slightly joined, the corolla-tube deeply included in the calyx.
         4. Petals naked; inflorescence of one or more distichous-flowered spikes or rarely simple and polystichous or even one-flowered. (Including *Cipuropsis*) ....*Tillandsia*.
         4. Petals each bearing one or two scales on the inner surface. (Including *Alcantarea*, *Thecophyllum*)_____*Vriesia*.
      3. Petals joined or closely agglutinated and simulating true fusion, the corolla-tube about equaling the calyx or longer; flowers always polystichous.
         5. Petals naked. (Including *Caraguata, Schlumbergera, Sodiroa, Massangea*).
            Guzmania.
         5. Petals bearing two scales _____*Mezobromelia*.
   2. Appendage of the seed apical, folded over at maturity; sepals strongly asymmetric in most species; flowers polystichous _____*Catopsis*.

1. Ovary only half superior, seeds plumose-appendaged at base and with a single filiform appendage at apex _____*Glomeropitcairnia*.

Subfamily 3. Bromelioideae.

1. Petals naked; flowers never in strobilate spikes.
   2. Filaments naked.
      3. Filaments not forming a tube; petals free or connate by their margins.
         4. Inflorescence elongate or if short (some species of *Streptocalyx*) then the flowers distichous; petals free.
            5. Inflorescence simple, lax.
               6. Flowers pedicellate; sepals symmetric; dry pollen-grains with a single longitudinal fold _____*Fernseea*.
               6. Flowers sessile; sepals asymmetric; pollen-grains with 2 pores _____ *Ronnbergia*.
            5. Inflorescence compound.
               7. Sepals not more than 3 mm. long; flowers minute, sessile or pedicellate; ovules few_____*Araeococcus*.
               7. Sepals 8-23 mm. long, flowers larger, sessile; ovules numerous _____ *Streptocalyx*.
         4. Inflorescence densely capitate, often involucrate; flowers never distichous; petals free or connate by their margins.
            8. Flowers on slender pedicels; inflorescence involucrate, sunk in the center of the rosette; petal-blades spreading, acute. (Including *Aregelia*)_____*Neoregelia*.
            8. Flowers sessile or subsessile.
               9. Petals free; sepals nearly or quite symmetric; stamens usually exserted; dry pollen-grains with a single longitudinal fold. (Including *Rhodostachys, Placseptalia*)_____*Ochagavia*.
               9. Petals more or less connate by their margins; sepals often asymmetric; stamens never longer than the petals.
                  10. Epigynous tube very short or lacking.
                     11. Petals fleshy, erect or in a few species of *Nidularium* spreading and acute; flowers all perfect.
                        12. Sepals symmetric, nearly or quite free; inflorescence usually lateral in the leaf-axils, sessile or nearly so. (Including *Hesperogreigia*).
                           Greigia.
                        12. Sepals asymmetric or highly connate or both together; inflorescence central, scapose but the scape often short and hidden beneath the broad inflorescence_____*Nidularium*.
                     11. Petals thin, widely spreading, obtuse, white or rarely yellow; flowers few in fascicles in the axils of leaf-like bracts, usually of two types, perfect and staminate, sepals much connate_____*Cryptanthus*.
                  10. Epigynous tube elongate; scape elongate, slender; inflorescence not involucrate_____*Andrea*.

12

3. Filaments forming a tube to which the fleshy petals are joined along their centers but with their margins free.
   13. Inflorescence compound, many-flowered, sessile or scapose, capitate or elongate. (Including *Karatas*).. *Bromelia.*
   13. Inflorescence simple, few-flowered, sessile, capitate .... *Deinacanthon.*

2. Filaments bearing 2 large appendages which overtop the anthers; inflorescence elongate, paniculate; flowers sessile; sepals asymmetric .... *Androlepis.*

1. Petals appendaged or when rarely naked then the flowers strobilate (in cone-like spikes).
  14. Ovaries always remaining distinct; inflorescence compound or simple.
    15. Ovary in small part superior; scape naked; inflorescence simple, strobilate, pseudolateral.. *Acanthostachys.*
    15. Ovary completely inferior.
     16. Scape-bracts foliaceous or the scape lacking; sepals always free.
      17. Epigynous tube very short or none; sepals acute or acuminate; second series of filaments connate with the petals.
       18. Petal-scales well developed; sepals nearly or quite symmetric, 10-20 mm. long; inflorescence or its spikes few-flowered, small. (Including *Cryptanthopsis, Sincoraea*) .... *Orthophytum.*
       18. Petal-scales vestigal; sepals definitely asymmetric, 25-35 mm. long; inflorescense or its spikes many-flowered, 6-15 cm. in diameter.
                      Some species of *Aechmea* subgenus *Purpurospadix.*
      17. Epigynous tube large; sepals rounded; filaments all free; inflorescence in the center of the rosette surrounded by colored bracts .... *Fascicularia.*
     16. Scape-bracts distinct from the leaves, or if there is no scape then the sepals much connate (species of *Aechmea*).
      19. Inflorescence involucrate; sepals nearly or quite free.
       20. Petals completely free... *Canistrum.*
       20. Petals partially connate above the base but free at base and exposing the base of the filaments of the first series.. *Wittrockia.*
      19. Inflorescence not involucrate or if somewhat so then the sepals much connate.
       21. Inflorescence compound; flowers in strobilate spikes, much compressed.
        22. Epigynous tube very small or lacking; pollen-grains with 2 or 4 pores.
                           Hohenbergia.
        22. Epigynous tube well developed; pollen-grains with more than 4 pores.
                             Gravisia.
       21. Inflorescence simple or if compound then the flowers not in strobilate spikes.
        23. Flowers sessile or if rarely pedicellate then the sepals free.
         24. Sepals mucronate or pungent or if blunt then small and the ovules long-caudate. (Including *Chevalieria, Disteganthus, Wittmackia*).
                              Aechmea.
        24. Sepals unarmed or soft-apiculate.
         25. Ovules numerous.
          26. Petals regular, erect or suberect; pollen-grains with pores; flowers sessile... *Quesnelia.*
          26. Petals either zygomorphic or recurved in a spiral; dry pollen-grains usually with a single longitudinal fold; flowers sessile or pedicellate.
                             Billbergia.
         25. Ovules few; flowers pedicellate, regular........................... *Neoglaziovia.*
        23. Flowers pedicellate; sepals much connate; pollen-grains with more than 4 pores.. *Portea.*

14. Ovaries fused with each other and with the fleshy bracts to form a syncarp; inflorescence with an apical coma, simple.
  27. Inflorescence with a small inconspicuous coma, never producing basal shoots; plant propagating by elongate rhizomes; petals bearing vertical folds........... *Pseudananas.*
  27. Inflorescence with a large conspicuous coma, often with basal shoots; rhizomes lacking; petals usually bearing well developed scales... *Ananas.*

13

FAMILY CHARACTERISTICS

In the evolution of *Bromeliaceae* the earliest forms and most primitive species are found in the subfamily Pitcairnioideae, more familiarly known as members of the genera Puya, Dyckia, Hechtia and Pitcairnia. Other members of this and other subfamilies are not mentioned here because they are seldom found in horticulture. In the Key on page 11 to 13 all the genera are listed under their respective subfamilies.

With a few exceptions all the members of this subfamily are exclusively terrestrial (growing in earth) or saxicolous (growing on rocks). There are, strange as it may seem, a few Pitcairnias, such as *P. heterophylla,* that sometimes may also be found growing on the larger branches and in the crotches of trees.

The plant form of most of the members of this group is a whorled rosette of stiff, spiny leaves. Exceptions to this general leaf type are in the genera Pitcairnia and Lindmania, which are generally rather grass-like plants in appearance and most of them have spineless leaves. Many of these spineless margined leaf species, however, may have very sharp spines and needle-like barbs at the base of their leaves.

The seeds of the Pitcairnias are very small and usually have small thin thread-like wings on each end. The Puyas have wings on at least three sides, while the Dyckia seeds, largest of the group, are completely surrounded with a thin flanged wing.

The fruits in this group are dry when mature; the three cells of each fruit burst open when ripe and the seeds are dispersed by wind.

The tubular flowers of this group run the range of the spectrum in color and in size from one half inch to six inches in length.

The culture of most of the members of this subfamily of terrestrials would be much the same as other bromeliads found living in acid soil. In horticulture we must take care, first, that no lime be used in the mixture where they are to be grown. There may be some exceptions to this rule, but so few, that it would not be a general cultural note. Being terrestrial these species develop a rather extensive root system, and potting material formula No. 3, page 23, should be used.

Dyckia

In this subfamily Dyckias have been the best known, horticulturally. They have been used for both inside and outside gardens, generally combined with cacti and other succulents. They seem to thrive under much neglect. All of the species being native principally to sunny areas in Brazil and Argentina, as well as their neighboring South American countries, they have the ability to withstand low temperatures and full light exposure when transferred to cultivation. Their small flowers are generally yellow or orange with petals fused into a tubular cup.

14

*Neoregelia carolinae
var. tricolor*

*Vriesea
heliconioides*

Guzmania hybrid

Aechmea fasciata

Aechmea miniata var. *discolor*

Aechmea × *"Fire ball"*

PUYA

Puyas are, for the most part, quite large plants and few of them can be grown to flowering maturity inside of a small greenhouse. However, they have been very successfully grown outdoors in the garden in temperate climates, where it is not too wet, notably in California where it has been amply proved that Puyas can withstand temperatures which go a few degrees below freezing.

Colors of the open petaled tubular flowers in this group predominate in blue, green and lavender, although some have white flowers; the size ranges from one to four inches in length.

PITCAIRNIA AND LINDMANIA

Pitcairnias, generally speaking, require more moisture and more shade than most other members of the terrestrial groups. In these genera there is yet to be done much experimentation before we are totally familiar with their hardiness in the lower temperatures. To date it has been found that a number do well in the outdoor gardens of Florida and California.

In the greenhouse, Pitcairnias are good foliage plants and in bloom remain colorful over a long period of time. The colors of their tubular flowers predominate in red and yellow, although a few are lovely in orange or white.

Lindmanias have very small delicate white, bell-shaped flowers borne on a many short-branched inflorescence and produce minute appendaged seeds. They are all terrestrial and are interesting but not showy.

HECHTIA

The Hechtias can take plenty of sun and will thrive among the rocks with well-drained soil in subtropical zones. Their gray spiny leaves become rosy-bronze in the right conditions making a splendid rosette addition to gardens in the sun. Hechtias are grown more for this decorative spiny rosette than for their tall spikes of flowers which are, in most species, inconspicuously small and whitish. Exceptions are found in *Hechtia purpusii* and *H. rosea* which have delicate sprays of pink flowers. Many of the Hechtias can take temperatures of freezing or slightly below.

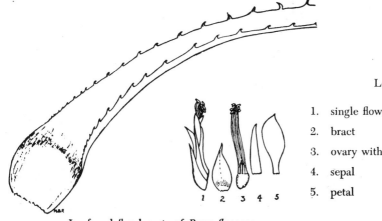

Legend

1. single flower
2. bract
3. ovary with pistil and stamens
4. sepal
5. petal

Leaf and floral parts of *Puya floccosa*

15

SUBFAMILY 2. TILLANDSIOIDEAE

This subfamily contains nearly one half of all the known species of bromeliads and the Tillandsias are at the top of this list with over 400 known species in that group. The Vriesias come next with nearly 150 known species. Other members of this subfamily known in horticulture are in the genera Guzmania, Catopsis, and Glomeropitcairnia.

The leaves of all the members of this group have smooth, spineless edges. They vary in length from one half inch to six feet. They may be flat and glossy or terete (round) and tomentose (fuzzy).

Most of the plants in this group are epiphytic, but a number of the largest species are terrestrial or saxicolous. Their flower colors predominate in violet-blue but follow the range of the spectrum.

Seeds of the Tillandsioideae have plumose appendages, or in the vernacular, little silky feather-like parachutes, often attached with a silken cord. All of them are plumose and are air-borne. The fruits are dry when mature, bursting open to expel their seeds, which are carried off like parachutes by air to new locations.

TILLANDSIA

Most of the Tillandsias are epiphytic, finding trees as their native habitat. However, the giant types, some of them like *Tillandsia grandis* with inflorescences up to ten and eleven feet, are saxicolous. Quite a number of them will grow equally well on rocks, on trees, or in well-drained soil.

There is one distinct xerophytic group, in the Tillandsias, which is found almost exclusively in the tree tops or in deciduous trees; these Tillandsias want much light, good aeration and little, if any, soil, especially the smaller types such as *T. ionantha, T. streptophylla, T. pruinosa, T. bulbosa, T. fasciculata* and countless other species that are, almost universally, rather heavily covered with gray peltate scales. Many of these have no central or basal leaf water reservoirs, so they, in the absence of rain, depend on heavy fogs or dew for most of their moisture which can be absorbed through their peltate scales.

This characteristic assists in making them good subjects for naturalistic plantings in trees in a tropical or subtropical garden; also exceptionally interesting and decorative specimens for culture in the greenhouses where they may be mounted on bark, tree limbs or potted in osmunda fiber.

Most of these species do not develop a heavy root system because in the wild their roots are principally hold-fast roots and do not serve as organs to seek food. These Tillandsias feed through their leaves rather than their roots.

In general, the flowers are tubular in shape, having violet-blue color. *T. Lindenii, T. decomposita* and others have larger spreading, iris-like blue-violet flowers. Those with the spreading open petals are usually quite fragrant. Many of the Tillandsia flowers last from three to five days.

The section of the Tillandsia group that has wider, thicker leaves which form a water reservoir at the base, require considerable light, although not all of them full sun. Thickness of leaves usually indicates more exposure to light and air, therefore they require a lesser amount of moisture. Leaves heavily covered with peltate scales need much light or sunlight and considerable aeration. If leaves are thin and glossy, they can generally be said to require shade.

16

VRIESIA

The Vriesias, in general, are shade loving and require less sun, their leaves being thin, glossy and spineless. Most of them are epiphytic, but the giant species may be saxicolus or terrestrial. All the species have leaf reservoirs for retaining water.

Nearly all the species do best when potted in osmunda fiber, for even though they like a great deal of water they require very good root drainage.

Yellow is the predominating flower color of those that bloom in the day time; those that flower at night are generally white. All Vriesia flowers are tubular in shape, remaining in bloom but one or two days. Flower spikes of Vriesias are usually flat and feather-like shaped, but those in the section formerly called Thecophyllum have compound inflorescences though the branches have but one to few flowers each. Many Vriesias hold their showy inflorescences from four to six months.

GUZMANIA AND CATOPSIS

Guzmanias have many plant characters in common with the Vriesias, smooth-leaved Tillandsias and Catopsis. Nearly all of them are epiphytic, requiring the same treatment as to potting material and exposure as for Vriesias.

Guzmanias have flowers in more than two rows in a single head, as *G. lingulata* or in several cluster branches as in *G. zahnii*. Flower colors are mainly white or yellow.

Most of the Guzmanias are rather high altitude plants while Catopsis species are generally found at low altitudes.

Catopsis flowers are small and white, borne on branched or unbranched stalks. They are interesting but not highly decorative.

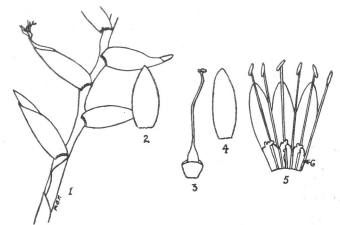

Legend

1. section of inflorecence
2. bract
3. pistil: stigma and ovary
4. sepal
5. 3 petals with stamens attached
6. nectar scales; two at base of each petal

Floral parts of *Vriesia psittacina*

17

SUBFAMILY 3. BROMELIOIDEAE

This group of bromeliads contains the greatest number of genera and therefore has the greatest range of plant forms. Their fruits are baccate or berry-like, usually in clusters of separate fruits, but are welded together in Ananas and Pseudananas. Some of the giant type Aechmeas have large compact heads of pineapple-like fruits but they are not actually welded together. All of the fruits of the subfamily are moist when ripe and their seeds are generally dispersed by birds or mammals, so they naturally have no wings or parachutes to carry them around. Some of them when ripe have rather a mucilaginous substance around the seeds especially in species of Billbergia, Aechmea, Neoregelia, Ananas, Bromelia, Cryptanthus, Orthophytum, Portea.

This group lives variously on the rocks, in the ground, or on the trees. Most of these Bromelioideae genera have liberal water reservoirs at the base of their leaves, but the ones such as Ananas, Pseudananas, Cryptanthus, Orthophytum, Neoglaziovia, Bromelia are strictly terrestrial plants and they have no water reservoir at the base of their leaves. Nidulariums, Canistrums, and Billbergias have a habitat, generally, low on trees or near the ground.

Most of the Bromelioideae develop a rather strong root system. These plants, generally speaking, are heavier than those in the Tillandsioideae. Also, they have a greater adaptation when grown horticulturally in pots. Most of the Billbergias, for instance, are epiphytic, and while they will grow well in osmunda fiber with similar treatment given Vriesias and Tillandsias, they adapt themselves successfully to soil culture. When they are grown in the porous mix such as suggested in the chapter under soils they will develop a much greater root system and will multiply much more rapidly than when growing as epiphytes on the limbs of trees.

In Aechmea we find the greatest range of types and the greatest number of species of any genera in the group of Bromelioideae. They may be found in the trees, on the rocks, or on the ground. This also applies to Hohenbergias, Quesnelias, and Gravisias which frequently grow in large compact colonies, sometimes covering large areas on the ground. Many species of this large group are showy and make excellent garden or house plant subjects. The inflorescence from flower to ripening of fruit often takes a period of from two to ten months. The flower colors may range throughout the spectrum; the flowers are usually small and cup-like in formation and often bloom over a long period, although each flower may last only a few hours. The fruits, however, may be several months in maturing; they are generally showy in connection with the brilliant bracts which decorate the inflorescence.

Neoregelias, Nidulariums and Canistrums derive their spectacular color display from the large colored leaf bracts which surround their compact submerged flower heads; this display may last eight to ten months.

There are three monotypic genera in this subfamily, each having but one species to represent it, Acanthostachys, Fernseea, and Neoglaziovia. Acanthostachys is generally epiphytic, rarely terrestrial; Fernseea is saxicolous and Neoglaziovia, terrestrial. The last two are rarely seen in cultivation. They can all be grown in the usual potting soil formula for Aechmeas.

18

BILLBERGIA AND AECHMEA

Two of the best known genera of Bromelioideae are Billbergia and Aechmea. Some common species of Billbergia such as *B. nutans* or *B. pyramidalis* is very often the first member of a fancier's collection. The tubular shaped Billbergias are easily handled and certainly require little attention; they are rarely temperamental and can put up with almost anyone, amateur or professional. Their seedlings may flower the second year, offshoots come the following year; they rarely fail to grow, flower and increase.

The flowers, ranging in blue-green and yellow, are always attractive and usually more so because of their showy pink or red scape bracts. The inflorescences generally mature and fade in the course of two weeks.

Aechmeas are equally easy to have as plant companions. Usually more showy and more interesting in plant form, they are in flower for much longer periods than Billbergias. Also, the colorful bracts and berries last for months as in *Ae. bracteata*, *Ae. fasciata* or *Ae. miniata var. discolor*.

Nidularium, Neoregelia, Canistrum, Wittrockia, Cryptanthus and Fasicularia are all genera which have their flowers in rather compact heads in the center of the plants, generally, rather low in the leaf rosettes. They can all take a similar potting medium suitable to Aechmeas.

Fasicularias enjoy the most sun, Nidulariums the most shade while Neoregelias, Canistrums, Wittrockias and Cryptanthi like plenty of light but slightly diffused or shaded.

Most Cryptanthus flowers are white and small, but the leaf patterns and colors of these "earth stars" endear themselves the year around to the plant lover.

PORTEA, QUESNELIA, GRAVISIA, HOHENBERGIA

Many interesting species are found in these four genera. Most of them, however, with the exception of such plants as *Quesnelia liboniana* are rather large for household decorative plants but are especially good for a specimen greenhouse plant or for the tropical patio and garden. They are all terrestrial, of simple culture as are the majority of the Bromelioideae. Their foliage, in most species, is plain green, but the large showy inflorescences make up for any lack of design or color in the leaves.

Ananas and Pseudananas, the pineapple and the false pineapple, are rather large for house culture with the exception of *Ananas ananasoides var. nana*, which is rare and is the smallest of all the pineapples.

BROMELIA

The genus Bromelia has some of the most spectacular members of all the flowering bromeliads, but most of the species are excessively large and should be grown outdoors in the warm zones in drained ground for proper maturing to flowering size. They have very heavily barbed leaves making a most efficient barrier when planted as a property line marker.

Nearly all of the members of the subfamily Bromelioideae have spiny leaf margins with the exception of two of the Ronnbergias. They have rather thin, smooth-edged leaves which are a definite contrast to any of the other members of this large subdivision.

The remaining genera in this subfamily are seldom seen except in the largest and rarest collections. In general, they do not need any different care than that of most of the members of Bromelioideae.

THE CULTIVATED AECHMEAS

VICTORIA PADILLA

THE FOLLOWING LIST was compiled from a number of sources: previous issues of the Bulletin, studies made by Mulford B. Foster and by Dr. Lyman B. Smith, catalogues in the American nursery trade, and from personal experiences in California and Florida.

It is almost impossible to describe exactly what a plant will look like, as variations in color, size, and texture are often found in one garden. But the descriptions given are what one normally might expect. Again, it is difficult to describe the exact growing conditions for a certain plant; a grower must be somewhat of an experimenter and find out for himself exactly what his plants need. All that we can do is point the way.

When reference is made to the fact that a plant is hardy what is meant is that it will grow outdoors the year round in a subtropical climate. "What is a subtropical climate?" one might ask. According to the noted plantsman of a half century ago, Dr. Franceschi, it is a climate where oranges and other citrus may be grown; in other words, it is a place of comparatively mild temperatures and where frosts are rare. Most of Florida, parts of Texas and Arizona, southern California, the countries surrounding the Mediterranean, parts of Australia and New Zealand and South Africa would hence fall into this category. But, again, there are climates within climates, and one must learn for himself, even if it be the hard way.

The date following each name refers to the year the plant was introduced into cultivation.

A. angustifolia (1838) Found growing on trees in rain forests, on rocks near rivers, and fairly high areas from Costa Rica to Brazil. A medium-sized plant. Leaves are fairly stiff (18 in. to 24 in.), spiny, light green spotted irregularly with purple. Flowers are negligible, but the plant is attractive in fruit, the white berries turning a vivid blue. It is interesting to note that some of the berries remain white; these contain no viable seeds. The plant needs a fairly humid atmosphere to be grown successfully, thus it does best in a greenhouse.

A. × *'Bert'* (1946) This is an early Foster cross *(A. orlandiana* × *A. fosteriana)* named for his son. A robust, upright, vase-like plant with heavily textured pale green leaves irregularly banded with purplish-brown markings. The leaves, reaching two feet, are edged with heavy, dark spines. The orange flower head rises above the leaves, but the plant does not need to be in bloom to be attractive. It is hardier than either of its parents and will accept any kind of treatment. This robust hybrid is not fussy, but it needs very well-drained potting material or will do well mounted on driftwood. It is a real tree climber in the warmer regions, but it can be raised successfully in the home.

A. blanchetiana (1840) Found growing on trees in the primeval jungle and in sandy areas near the sea in Baia, Brazil. A large plant and very interesting with its branched inflorescence, but it is only for those who have a large greenhouse or who can grow it outdoors in a warm climate. Its pale green leaves attain a length of three feet.

Aechmea chantinii

A. blumenavii (1952) Found growing on trees and rocks in the open forests of southern Brazil. A cold-resistant little gem with firm smooth green leaves tipped with purple seldom exceeding one foot in length. Its soft pink inflorescence with yellow flowers last in color for several weeks. It is amenable to all growing conditions. Hardy.

A. bracteata (1844) Also known as *A. schiedeana*. Found growing in coastal regions either in dense masses on rocks or on trees from Mexico to Colombia. It is a large robust plant which in its native habitat attains a spread of from three to five feet. Its bright green leaves, armed wih large prominent widely-set teeth form a cylindrical rosette from which emerges a slender branched inflorescence bearing greenish-yellow flowers and bright red bracts which last for months. There is a red form of this plant which is very attractive. This is a stunning Aechmea for those who can grow it outdoors; it can stand slight frost and is not particular as to location. The berries are said to be edible, but the birds generally get them first. The hollow ellipsoid leaf rosette holds much water which carries it through drought periods.

A. bromeliifolia (1805) Epiphytic or terrestrial, it is usually found growing on rocks or on ground in forests from Guatemala to Argentina. Twelve-to-twenty-inch-

Aechmea mariae reginae

long, grey-green leaves with hooked teeth form a handsome pear-shaped rosette about two feet high. The flower stalk rises above the foliage to form a pinecone-shaped spike of white with lemon-yellow flowers, which soon turn black. If not allowed to sucker too freely, this Aechmea assumes a very stunning form. A hardy plant, it is not fussy as to growing medium. It is a worth-while plant for the collector.

A. calyculata (1865) Grows on trees in the rain forests of Argentina and Brazil. A medium-sized plant with stiff green tubular foliage. The flower stalk is scarlet-red with a thistle-type head of yellow flowers, lasting in color for a long time. Needs good light and will take even some direct sunlight. Hardy.

A. caudata var. variegata (1935) *Originally known as A. forgettii.* This variegated form is a sport of the original type *A. caudata var. caudata,* found growing in the forests and restingas (dwarf coastal forests) of southern Brazil. This variegated form is a medium-large, handsome plant with stiff, arching leaves (18 in. to 30 in.) that are light green with longitudinal creamy stripes, with a decided pinkness on the offshoots and near the base of mature plants. The inflorescence is compact and branched with golden yellow flowers, appearing at the end of a long white mealy stem. This is a hardy plant which will take a few degrees of frost. It makes a stunning planter subject for the patio or lanai in warmer climates; it makes a good house plant if given sufficient room. Like many variegated forms, its seed produces only green plants, but it suckers freely. An extremely shy bloomer, but a valuable plant for its foliage. Not fussy as to potting medium.

A. chantinii (1878) Found on the trees in the Amazon valley forests of Brazil, Colombia, and Ecuador. Although in cultivation in Europe for the past 70 years, it was rarely seen. Just lately introduced into the American trade, it is probably one of the most sought-after Aechmeas in the U. S. today. A medium-sized plant, its stiff green leaves are boldly banded with silvery white and olive to dark green; its erect branched inflorescence is covered with rich orange colored bracts. Flowers are yellow and white. There is much variation in the type of growth, one nursery offering several phases. Despite its robust appearance, this plant needs good care, much light, and perfect drainage. Tree fern or osmunda is the preferred pot mixture. An extremely beautiful plant, *Aechmea chantinii* is the center of attraction whether in bloom or not.

A. coelestis (1856) Found growing on trees and rocks, sometimes in full light, in Brazil. A medium-sized, urn-shaped plant with stiff, moss-green leaves, it has a flower head of lavender-blue flowers that is stunning. The variety *albo-marginata* is similar to the plain leaved variety except that the leaves have white margins, making it a very attractive foliage plant. This form is a little more difficult to grow; where the water is hard, the leaves tend to tip-burn. It does best in tree fern or osmunda. An excellent house plant. Hardy.

A. comata (1865) Found growing on coastal rocks and dunes in full sun in southern Brazil. Formerly known as *A. lindenii*. A tall, tubular, vigorous plant with grey-green leaves and a brilliant yellow and orange cylindrical flower head, this is a collector's item rather than a house plant. Does best when it can be grown outside and is quite cold hardy.

A. cylindrata (1891) Found growing on trees and on the floor of the forests of southern Brazil. An open rosette plant with wide green leaves tipped with a black spot. The inflorescence is cylindrical, the flowers are blue and the fruit, rose. The flowers all open in a few days, but the fruits last for two or more months. Hardy.

A. dealbata (1889) From central Brazil. A tall tubular plant resembling a Billbergia in form, it was at one time compared with *A. fasciata*. The upper side of the leaves is dark green, the underside, a purplish brown with occasional cross bands of silver. The inflorescence is lavender-pink. A very handsome plant, whether in bloom or not, it deserves a place in every collection. Because of its graceful form and medium size, it makes an idea house plant. Does best in tree fern or osmunda.

A. distichantha var. schlumbergeri (1879) Found growing on the ground in open woods in Brazil, Paraguay, and Argentina. This is a large plant (to three feet) with quite stiff, slightly arching leaves of a pale green, lighter when grown in a strong light. Definitely not a house plant, it does well when planted in the soil in the open garden and will take full sun. It suckers freely and in a short time will make a sizable clump. The amethyst-violet flowers on old-rose bracts are very attractive. Among the hardiest of the Aechmeas. The varieties of this species, var. *glaziovii* or var. *canalyculata* are much smaller in size and are better suited for the collector.

Padilla

R. Foster

A. × 'Foster's Favorite'

A. marmorata
Now *Quesnelia marmorata*

A. fasciata (1826)   Found on trees in the rain forests of Brazil.   This has been a favorite house plant in Europe ever since its introduction where for years and still today it is known as *Billbergia rhodocyanea*.   So popular has been this plant that its name is almost synonymous with bromeliad.   The type plant is medium sized, with silver banded green leaves and a pink inflorescence with pale French blue flowers that never fail to bloom each summer.   The spike lasts in color for a good half-year. It is indeed the perfect plant for home, patio, or greenhouse.   It does best in osmunda or tree fern, but some growers are successful raising it in soil if it is kept moist. Needs good light, but little, if any direct sun.   In late years several horticultural forms of this plant have been introduced.   Highly popular is that known as the Belgium variety, in which the entire plant seems dusted with a silvery whittish powder and no cross marking are discernible.   Another variety is *purpurea* from Brazil. This form differs only in that the leaves are completely suffused with dark purplish-rose.   There are two variegated varieties: *albo-marginata,* with leaves having borders of ivory-white bands, and *variegated* with longitudinal bands throughout the leaf.

A. filicaulis (1864)   Found only in the mountain forests of Venezuela.   This is a medium-sized plant with soft green leaves which take on a bronze hue if grown in full light.   The inflorescence is suspended on a thread-like scape, which may hang from the plant for nearly 6 feet.   The bracts are a bright rosy red; the flowers are white and suprisingly large.   This delightful plant should be grown where it can hang and where the breeze can catch the flowers, turning them into so many white butterflies..   It requires ordinary care, but does best in a greenhouse, although it does grow outdoors in protected tropical areas.

A. fosteriana (1939)   From the coastal forests of central Brazil.   A tubular formed

24

plant to 24 inches high, its pale green to reddish-green leaves are mottled with purple-brown zig-zag markings and are edged with heavy green spines. The flower pike is a panicle of crimson bracts and rich yellow flowers. This is one of the fussiest of all Aechmeas, but is so beautiful that all should attempt growing it. It probably does best in the greenhouse, but has been grown very successfully outdoors in protected areas. Does best, it would seem, when grown on the dry side, but the grower must experiment to find out what is best for plant.

A. × *'Foster's Favorite'* (1949)   The first patented bromeliad, this Aechmea is a cross between *A. racinae* and *A. victoriana var. discolor*. It is the favorite of everyone who grows it, for it is amenable to most growing conditions. Its highly polished, wine-red leaves make it at all times a beautiful plant. The inflorescence is semipendant, the deep purple-blue flower-petals giving way to dark red berries which last in color for months. A winter bloomer, it is an ideal size for a house plant, leaves seldom exceeding 20 inches in length.

A. fulgens var. fulgens (1841)   Found growing on the trees or ground in Brazil. A small to medium-sized plant, this is a tubular-formed Aechmea with pale green leaves. Its inflorescence is a panicle of red berries topped with blue petals. Long lasting, fairly hardy, it will withstand any planting mixture so long as it is well drained, and will even take some neglect.

A. fulgens var. discolor (1889)   Found growing on the trees or ground in Brazil. This is a medium-sized plant with out-spreading fairly stiff, leathery leaves, dusty green on the upper side and a glossy purple covered with a whitish powder on the under side. The dark purple flowers make a stunning head on the top of a foot-long carmine stalk. The rose-colored berries last in color for many months. A perfect house plant, it will take adverse conditions and is attractive whether in flower or not. It does best when given considerable light and can be well grown in a loose soil. A sporadic bloomer, but generally flowers in spring.

A. lamarchei (1889)   Found on ground and the light forests of Brazil. Also known as *A. lagenaria*. This plant is quite variable in form. It has a pinecone-type flower-head, the yellow petals turning black a day or two after blooming. Often the flower head is yellow, white, and black all at the same time. Scape bracts are a brilliant red. A hardy plant, it is an interesting item for any collector.

A. lasseri (1951)   Found on trees in the high forests of Venezuela. An attractive, smallish plant, it is chiefly notable for its pendant inflorescence, which may hang two to three feet. The inflorescence consists of rose-red bracts, the flowers are greenish-white, and the berries are bluish. The soft gray-green leaves turn reddish if given sufficient light. Will grow in loose, moist soil. Hardy.

A. luddemanniana (1866)   Found growing on the ground and on the trees of Central America. A beautiful dignified plant which when well grown will have a spread of three feet. The arching leaves are a blend of green and bronze, turning more brilliant when the plant is grown outdoors. The flower spike rises erect above the plant, the rose and green flowers turning into a dense head of blue and white berries which finally become a startling purple that lasts for months. Not particular as to growing medium. Makes an attractive house plant.

Aechmea mexicana in its native habitat

A. mariae reginae (1864)   Grows on the ground or on the trees in Costa Rica.   This is a large, imposing plant suitable only for the large conservatory, the leaves often measuring 3 feet in length.   They are broad, light green, and edged with stout spines. The erect, handsome flower spike has watermelon-pink bracts topped by a cylindrical head of red-tipped berries with violet flowers.   This stunning plant is called "Flor de Santa Maria" and is highly thought of by the natives of Costa Rica.   It likes light and is not partial as to growing medium.   *See: Brom. Bull. article — Vol. V, No. 6 (1955). Color photo — Vol. VI, No. 6 (1956)*

A. marmorata (1855) Found on trees in Brazilian forests.   This tall, tubular plant, which looks more like a Billbergia than it does an Aechmea, is sometimes called the "Grecian Vase," which it most definitely resembles.   From grey-green leaves, cross-banded with darker green, arises a beautiful arching stalk bearing bright pink bracts and blue flowers. Any very well drained potting medium seems to make it happy. Needs good light.   This is an outstandingly lovely plant and should do well in the house.

A. mertensii (1818)   Found growing in the ground and on trees in the forests of Trinidad and northern South America.   Dr. Smith states that this is one of the most variable species in all the Bromeliaceae because of the extreme range in the size of flowers and in the size and density of the inflorescence.   The plant is medium sized with bright green scaly leaves edged with dark brown teeth. The spike, (one foot in height) is covered with red bracts and is topped by a dense cylindrical flower head of yellow flowers. The berries upon maturing turn a deep chicory blue. A collector's item.

A. mexicana (1886) Epiphytic and terrestrial in forests, often exposed to full sun, from Mexico to Ecuador. This large, handsome plant should be grown outdoors in considerable light to attain its maximum beauty. Indoors the leaves are a pale mottled green; outdoors they become tinged with vivid red. The flower spike at the end of a bold, erect stem is bright crimson which turns to pearl-like berries. An adaptable plant, this Aechmea will grow under almost any kind of condition. However, it cannot be considered a house plant unless ample room is provided, as the leaves sometimes measure three feet. Hardy. *See: Vol. V, No. 6 (1955)*

A. miniata var. *discolor* (1857) Epiphytic in Bahia, Brazil. An outstanding, medium-sized plant, with outspreading leaves of rich olive-green on top and glossy maroon underneath. The inflorescence is an erect spike of berry-like fruit with blue flowers, the berries turning red and lasting many months. This is a highly decorative plant which does very well in the home. Does best in a well-drained potting mixture and needs good light. Hardy. *A. miniata* var. *miniata* is also a very fine subject. It grows somewhat larger and the leaves are a lovely delicate green.

A. miniata var. *discolor* × *A. calyculata* This is one of the first hybrids using *A. miniata* var. *discolor* as one of the parents. Its background is not known, but it has been grown in southern California for a number of years. A stunning plant with its tall orange-yellow flower head, it is larger than either of its parents, the dark maroon and green leather-like leaves measuring a good two feet. A hardy plant, it will take considerable light, cold, and neglect. This is a highly decorative Aechmea and does well under average home conditions. *(See: photo in Handbook)*

A. miniata var. *discolor* × *A fulgens* var. *discolor* (1954) This hybrid of unknown origin was introduced into the trade as *A.* × *maginalii*. It is a fine cross combining the best qualities of both parents. Leaves are apple-green on upper side, soft maroon beneath. The bracts are salmon red, the flowers a bright blue which turn into orange berries lasting for several months. L'ke *A. miniata* var. *discolor*. it is a dependable bloomer.

A. nudicaulis (1753) Found growing on trees and rocks, sometimes in full sun, from Mexico and the West Indies into Venezuela. The stiff, spined, grey-green leaves form a tubular rosette from which emerges the brilliant inflorescence of bright red bracts and yellow flowers. The flowers do not last so long in color as do those of other Aechmeas, but no other Aechmea puts on a brighter display. The variety *A. nudicaulis* var. *cuspidata,* confined to South America, is similar except that the plant tends to be heavier with broader leaves which also show slight horizontal silver markings. It was first introduced in 1879. A third variety, *A. nudicaulis* var. *aureo-rosea.* was found in Brazil in 1881. It differs from the others in that it is smaller, its leaves are more obviously cross-banded, and the inflorescence is stiffer, the frosty-white berries turning a pinkish color. All three varieties are hardy and will take almost any kind of treatment.

A. organensis (1880) Found growing on the ground and on the trees from Organ Mts.

Padilla

Aechmea nudicaulis

to the extreme southern part of Brazil. This is a medium-sized plant with stiff, dark green leaves. The flowers are blue and the fruits are burnt orange. A hardy, robust Aechmea.

A. orlandiana (1939) Discorved by Mulford Foster growing in the forests of central Brazil and named in honor of the city, which due to his efforts has become the home of the world's largest collection of living bromeliads. "Bizarre" best describes this Aechmea with its zigzag markings of dark chocolate on pale green leaves. The lower leaves of this medium-sized plant tend to droop, a feature which further distinguishes it from others. The striking orange spike of white and yellow flowers appears in winter. This plant is sometimes difficult to grow, but is well worth the effort. It definitely needs good light. Does well on bromeliad trees, fern, or soil.

A. ornata var. *ornata* (1843) Found growing on trees or on the ground in the forests and restingas of Brazil. Formerly known as *A. hystrix*. A hardy, medium-sized plant with stiff olive-green foliage, it has been referred to as "the porcupine Aechmea." Flowers are pale rose or red. When it is out of flower, this Aechmea can be mistaken for an agave: It is a tough plant that can stand rough treatment and full sun.

A. pectinata (1879) Found growing on trees and on the ground in the restingas of Brazil. An open, stiff rosette with mottled soft green leaves which turn rose in the center, this Aechmea may attain a spread of two feet. It has a compact pineapple-like head on a medium spike; flowers are green. This plant is an extremely shy bloomer, but it is worth growing for its foliage alone. Makes an excellent yard plant in temperate regions.

A. pimenti-velosoi (1952) Grows on trees in the southern forests of Brazil. This is a charming small plant with stiff green leaves forming a tubular rosette. Has a rather compact cylindrical head of yellow flowers. Not a very fussy grower and hardy.

A. pineliana var. *pineliana* (1854) Found growing in the forests of Brazil. This is an attractive, medium-sized hardy plant with slender leaves of grey-pink. In the sun, the leaves tend to turn a rich rose. The inflorescence consists of a stiff, erect stem, pinkish bracts and a cone-shaped head of yellow flowers. Conspicuous dark spines enhance the beauty of the leaves. There is a miniature form of his plant known as *A. pineliana* var. *minuta,* which has a colorful gray-bronze foliage. Not fussy as to potting medium.

A. penduliflora (1830) Found growing on trees and on the ground in the rain forests from Costa Rica to Brazil. Formerly known as *A. schultesiana.* This is a medium-sized Aechmea with strap-like leaves of a rich green, turning maroon in strong light. It tends to be variable, however, both in size and coloration. The flowers are negligible, the charm of the plant being in the cluster of whitish berries which soon turn cobalt blue and which last for many months. Not a fussy grower. Hardy. *(See photo: Vol VII, No. 6, 1957)*

A. pubescens (1879) Found growing in trees in partially cleared forests and on the ground in moist open woods from Honduras to Colombia. This is an attractive medium-sized plant with a rather loose but graceful rosette of broad dusty green leaves with pubescent scales. It is quite variable in both size and coloring ac-

cording to its native habitat. In some plants the leaves are plain green; in others they are a reddish brown. The branched inflorescence, which is both unusual and attractive, appears at the end of a thin red stem, the straw-colored petals of the flowers turning to blue berries which last in color for many months. Not a fussy grower, it is hardy. Prefers good light.

A. purpureo-rosea (1834) Epiphytic in the coastal forests of central Brazil. This medium-sized Aechmea has deep green heavily textured leaves, edged with black spines, which form a tall tubular rosette. The mealy coated scape bears a long panicle of rosy-red bracts and lavender flowers. An attractive plant, it is hardy and not fussy as to culture.

A. racinae var. *racinae* (1940) Epiphytic in the rain forests of Brazil. This attractive Aechmea, often called "Christmas Jewels" because of its habit of blooming at the holiday season, was originally named in honor of Racine Foster, its co-discoverer. This is a small

L. Cutak

Aechmea pubescens

29

plant with soft, glossy green leaves. The inflorescence appears at the end of a pendant stem; the yellow and black flowers turning into brilliant orange-red berries which last in color for many months. To display the inflorescence to its best advantage this plant should be grown in a hanging basket or else attached to a bark slab or a bromeliad tree. It prefers semi-shade.

A. ramosa var. ramosa (1889) Found growing on trees in central Brazil. This is a stunning Aechmea which seems to be perfectly hardy. A medium-sized to large plant, its foliage may vary in color from rose-pink to soft green. The inflorescence which rises well above the leaves on an orange scape, has many branches. The colorful inflorescence of greenish-yellow berries and yellow flowers may be likened to a swarm of bees and is attractive for about six months. An easy Aechmea to grow, it is not fussy as to the care given it.

A. recurvata There are a number of varieties of this particular Aechmea, all of which are native to Brazil. *A recurvata* var. *recurvata* (1856) grows on rocks and trees and resembles a Dyckia in form and leaf texture. It is a small to medium-sized plant with spiny edges and an infloresence completely exserted above the leaf-sheaths. The floral bracts are serate. *A. recurvata* var. *benrathii* (1866) is found growing on coastal rocks in full sun. This is a tiny plant and could easily be mistaken for a Tillandsia. The stiff green leaves form a tight head, the rose flowers being partly hidden by the recurved leaves. The inner leaves turn red when the plant is about to bloom — an unusual trait for this genus. *A. recurvata* var. *ortgiesii* (1899) is found growing on trees and rocks in part to full sun. This is a medium-sized plant with numerous leaves of a shiny rich green which form a tight rosette. The inflorescence of red bracts and berry-like fruit are almost or wholly included by the leaf sheaths. All these plants are hardy and easy to grow.

A. × 'Royal Wine' (1947) This handsome hybrid by Mulford B. Foster is a cross between *A. miniata* var. *discolor* and *A. victoriana* var. *discolor*. It is a beautiful plant with outstanding broad leathery leaves which are pale olive-green on their upper side and lacquered wine-red underneath. The partly pendant inflorescence has blue flowers which turn into deep orange berries. This is a fine plant for the home, as it is as hardy as either of its parents and will withstand a certain amount of neglect. It likes light, but not direct sun. Is attractive whether in flower or not.

A. tessmanii (1927) Found growing on trees in dense forests and on river banks in Colombia and Peru. The stiff, gray-green leaves form a medium-sized tight rosette. The branched inflorescence of orange-red berry-like fruit with yellow flowers makes this a most desirable plant. It does well in either soil or tree fern, but where the water is highly alkaline, tree fern is recommended. Although it is a fussy plant and not hardy, it is none the less well worth trying.

A. tillandsioides var. *tillandsioides* (1830) Epiphytic in the rain forests from Mexico to Brazil. The shiny green leaves and branced inflorescence with its red bracts, white flowers and blue berries make this a most attractive plant. It is a stocky Aechmea, known sometimes as "the red, white, and blue bromeliad," for its fruits ripen one at a time. Another variety, *A. tillandsiodies* var. *kienastii*, is similar, but smaller and the inflorescence is appreciably shorter and with fewer branches. This is the best variety for the house. This Aechmea does well in soil or tree fern.

A. triangularis (1940) A native of Brazil, where it is found growing on trees. This striking bromeliad is a member of that group of Aechmeas to which *A. lamarchei*, *A. bromeliifolia*, *A. chlorophylla*, and others belong. All have a compact cylindric, strobilate flower head, the petals of which turn jet black the second or third day after coming into bloom — the inflorescence thus being at least three colors at once. In

Aechmea distichantha

Aechmea tillandsioides

Aechmea racinae
("Christmas Jewels")

Billbergia × *"Fantasia"*

Billbergia pyramidalis

Billbergia porteana

Guzmania sanguinea

Guzmania lingulata var. *minor*

Guzmania dissitiflora

Guzmania berteroniana

Guzmania musaica

Guzmania zahnii

the case of *A. triangularis,* the petals are purple and the flower stem a brilliant red. This is a medium-sized plant with stiff, heavily spiked, bright green leaves which form a rather tight but graceful rosette.   The leaves are quite broad at the base, but sharply come to a point.   A stunning plant, whether in bloom or not, it is rather tender despite its robust appearance. It prefers fir bark or tree fern.   It did best for this writer when it was left forgotten under the bench, although for most growers it does well in a strong light.

A. victoriana (1941) Found growing on rocks and on the ground in Brazil. This is a medium-sized Aechmea with bright green leaves.   The inflorescence is unusual, first showing as a semi-pendant string of red beads, clustered on the stem.   The beads, which break out into peach and purple flowers, later turn into deep brownish-black berries.   The cluster of fruits is often 6 to 8 inches long.   A fairly hardy plant, it is easy to grow, not being fussy as to potting mixture. *A. victoriana* var. *discolor* is a red-leaved variety, which is of unusual attractiveness.

A. weilbachii var. *weilbachii* (1879)   Found growing in central Brazil.   This is a fairly hardy species.   This variety has leaves that are entirely green.   Better known is *A. weilbachii* var. *leodiensis* (1887) whose leaves are bronze-red tinged with purple The inflorescence consists of a stem with crimson bracts and a panicle of orchid-shaded berries and flowers. This is a vigorous plant which suckers freely and is one that should be in every collection.

Aechmea pineliana var. *minuta*

31

A WORD FOR THE BILLBERGIA

VICTORIA PADILLA

WHEN IT WAS ANNOUNCED THAT BILLBERGIAS were going to be discussed at some length in this bulletin, several society members threw up their hands in what amounted to holy horror. According to their way of thinking the subject of Billbergias was too elementary for a publication of this sort and not enough people bothered to raise these bromeliads any more.

It certainly is true that Billbergias are among the easiest bromeliads to grow, that they multiply rapidly, that they propagate easily from seed or offshoot, and that it is next to impossible to kill a Billbergia by mistreatment. Perhaps growing a Billbergia does not present a challenge as does a Vriesea or a Guzmania, but a collection of fine Billbergias well grown can be a source of great satisfaction, as they rank among the most beautiful of the entire bromeliad family.

For most of us—in the United States that is—Billbergias were the first bromeliads that we knew and grew. In Florida it was probably *B. pyramidalis* that attracted attention, whereas in California *B. nutans* is still used by the uninitiated as a synonym for bromeliad. In Australia, too, *B. nutans* grows in great abundance. In fact, rare is the garden in the temperate regions that does not have a clump or two of Billbergias growing in some protected area.

Billbergias are found growing natively from Mexico to Argentina, the greatest number and the most colorful, however, being found in central Brazil, Dr. Lyman B. Smith listing 53 species and varieties in his *Bromeliaceae of Brazil*. Although these bromeliads are classified as epiphytes, they seem to grow with equal ease perched on trees, clinging to rocks or stumps, or rooted on the ground. Indeed, Billbergias are good-natured plants and appear to adapt themselves to any growing condition in which they find themselves.

When brought under cultivation they are just as amenable. Most of them are quite hardy and will do well in the open garden if given a light porous soil—the kind used for begonias or fuchsias. For the most part, Billbergias do best under lath house conditions, although some species require an intensity of light just short of direct sun light to bring out the full beauty of their coloring. Billbergias grown in deep shade, as a rule, seldom attain their optimum potentialities in the way of flowering and foliage coloration.

Because of their adaptability Billbergias can easily be grown with other plants that like similar conditions, such as ferns, camellias, azaleas, and even succulents. Some Billbergias are effective if grown in clumps in a partly shaded spot or rockery others—those whose foliage and form are of singular beauty—are seen to best advantage when just a few shoots are allowed to remain in a container. *B. leptopoda* is an excellent example of a Billbergia which should not be allowed to get crowded in the pot. Some like to multiply in the crotch of a tree or attached to a palm, and others make stunning hanging basket subjects. They all make good house plants.

Billbergias are the most easily identifiable of all bromeliads. Their leaves are fewer in number (seldom exceeding eight) than in most other species and are with only a few exceptions tubular in form. The foliage is generally banded with gray cross bars, although irregular spotting and blotching are by no means uncommon, as in *B. saundersii, B. amoena* var. *viridis, B. leptopoda,* etc. Most species have a pendent inflorescence with large brilliantly colored bracts. *B. pyramidalis* and *B. horrida* and their hybrids are among the few exceptions that have an erect flower spike. The inflorescence, though lasting but a short while, is always spectacular. From bracts, ranging in color from green to white and from pink to red, emerge the flowers tubular in form with the ends of the petals curled back. The predominating shades of the petals are purple, blue, yellow, green, and white.

There has been more confusion over the nomenclature of Billbergias than with any other genus. This has been due, no doubt, to the ease with which these plants can be hybridized. Billbergias propagate readily from seed, and the seedlings mature and flower in three years, with the exception of *B. zebrina*, *B. meyeri*, and *B. porteana*. In California there were a number of early growers of bromeliads, such as Charles Case, Richard Atkinson, and others, who produced a number of very fine Billbergias but kept no record of thei parentage. Today, California gardens contain many of these excllent hybrids, but what they are no one knows for sure. This situation probably also may be found existing in Florida, Australia, and other temperate countries.

It is not only the hybrids which cause confusion, however, for a species even in its native habitat is sometimes not readily recognizable. One plant growing high on a tree and another growing closer to the ground may appear so different that they would appear to be two different species. This is due to the fact that different growing conditions sometimes tend to change the appearance of a Billbergia so radically that identification is not easily made. Any interesting experiment is to take a Billbergia (*B. amoena* is excellent for this purpose) that has several offshoots, separate the little pups and plant them in various locations about the garden—in the sun, in the shade, in the greenhouse, in the open garden, etc.—and note the difference in appearance as the plants mature. Some will have long leaves, some, short; some will have wide leaves, others will be reed-like; some plants will have interesting mottled foliage, some will be plain green. In fact, it will be hard to believe that all these plants were offshoots of the same mother plant. It is readily understandable, therefore, that it is easy for the amateur to become confused when it comes to recognizing his plants. Luckily, present-day nurserymen are attempting to be scientific in the naming of their Billbergias, though, unfortunately, error does still exist in some instances. On the Continent, a number of bromeliads are classified as Billbergias, when, in truth, they are of a different genus. The two best known examples of this mistake in nomenclalture in the use of the name *B. rhodocyanea* for *A. fasciata* and *B. forgettii* for *A. caudata* var. *variegata*.

During the past few years a number of Billbergias have been reclassified and re-named. The following are a few of the names which have become obsolete:

B. amabilis — now *B. vittata*
B. bonplandiana — formerly used for *B. nutans* and *B. distachia* var. *straussiana*
B. calophylla — formerly used for *B. vittata*
B. caespitosa — formerly used for *B. distachia*.
B. leopoldii — obsolete but still occasionally found being used erronesouly for *B. vittata*, *B. brasiliensis*. and others.
B. minuta — former name for *B. nutans*
B. quintissima — now *B. macrocalyx*
B. rohaniana — now *B. vittata*
B. rubro-cyanea — formerly erroneously applied to *B. saundersii*
B. thyrsoides — now *B. pyramidalis* var. *concolor*.
B. zonatus — now *B. vittata*

BILLBERGIA SPECIES

B. amoena — This is a very variable species, both as to color and size. The type is a plain green tubular plant of medium size. The flowers all have a green ridged ovary, blue green sepals, and blue tipped petals. *B. amoena* and its many varietal forms, several of which have been named, are highly desirable bromeliads. *B. amoena* var. *rubra* was discovered in the state of Espirito, Santo, Brazil, in 1939 by M. B. Foster. It is two to three times as large as some of the other varieties of *B. amoena.* The rich red leaves with white and yellow spots may be two to three feet in height.

B. amoena var. *viridis* is the most colorful of all the varieties of *B. amoena* and is certainly one of the most decorative of all Billbergias. The spotted and barred, green and rose foliage makes it an outstanding bromeliad. Its inflorescence differs from that of other varieties in that the flowers have plain green petals.

B. buchholtzii — This plant does not appear in any listings of commercial growers, but Oakhurst Gardens in southern California has for sale three variations. Whether these belong under the listing of *B. buchholtzii* is not known. However, the plants so named are very attractive. No. 1 is a dwarf form with brilliant orange-scarlet bracts and deep blue flowers. When well established, it will have several blooming periods a year. No. 2 has tall, light green foliage, rose bracts and lavender flowers. No. 3 has very attractive leaves of huge size, deep green with bronze shadings and barred transversely with gray. It becomes purplish in the sun. The flowers are violet with pink bracts.

B. distachia — This is an old-time favorite that has been in cultivation for over seventy years. As can be noted from the illustration it is a medium-sized plant with compact tubes and pendant flower heads. The leaves are green tinged with purple and covered with a whitish scurf; the flowers are green, tipped with blue and the bracts are rose. There are four varieties of *B. distachia* listed: *B. distachia* var. *distachia,* with lavender green leaves, *B. distachia* var. *straussiana* with green petals, *B. distachia* var. *concolor* with green leaves, and *B. distachia* var. *maculata* with spotted leaves. Fantastic Gardens in its most recent catalogue lists a fourth variety which it calls B. *distachia* var. *rubra.* It is described as a plant of "upright tubular growth. Leaves look like purple haze in the sky with silver clouds shining thru. Pendulous flowers rise above the urn and are tipped with blue, rose bracts. Unusual color effect."

B. elegans — A husky appearing, rock-gray, saw-toothed tubular plant, this Billbergia is one of striking contrasts, for its dainty flowers seem out of keeping with the heavy foliage. This species is different from all others in that the flowers are produced from the axils of the bracts rather than terminally. The flower is long, pendent and of a delightfully different green; the bracts are a clear shade of rose. The buds have dark blue tips.

B. euphemiae — This Billbergia has been popular for many years. As it is a stoloniferous plant, it is attractive when grown in hanging baskets. The wide, reflexed blue-green leaves are about a foot long. The inflorescence is especially noteworthy, the bracts being a powdery rose and the flowers an enchanting violet. Two new varieties of this species have recently been introduced by Mr. Foster: *B. euphemia* var. *purpurea,* which differs from the type in that it has reddish-purple leaves and does not have gray bands: and *B. euphemiae* var. *saundersioides,* which had long narrow leaves prominently spotted with white and pink.

34

Bacher

Billbergia distachia

B. horrida — This attractive plant received its name from the large spines on its leaf margins. It is a medium-sized plant with stiff, green leaves with indistinct gray bands. It is quite tubular in form although the leaves flare slightly at the top. The inflorescence is erect; the flowers are a transparent green. *B. horrida* var. *tigrina* is similar to *B. horrida* except that the leaves are maroon-brown with distinct silver-gray bands. The flowers are fragrant at night—an unusual characteristic among Billbergias. Both of these Billbergias are interesting plants and worthy of a place in every collection.

B. iridifolia var. *concolor* — This is a delightful little Billbergia which should be in every collection. Its color scheme is particularly attractive; its leaves are soft grey, the bracts a delicate pink, and the flowers a clear yellow. Concolor in this instance means that the petals of the flower are one pure color. Suitable for pot culture.

B. lietzei — This is another charming small type of Billbergia, and this one is usually in bloom at the holiday season. Its curled, light green leaves are dotted with yellow; its flowers are a bright cerise. It does not multiply too rapidly; thus its value as a small pot is at once obvious.

B. leptopoda — Again we have another gay little Billbergia that is best as a pot specimen. It is often referred to as "the permanent wave plant," as its leaves, from a tubular center, curl back as though trained to that effect. The plant seldom reaches over 12 inches in height. Its green leaves are spotted with white; its erect inflorescence bears red bracts and blue and yellow flowers. This Billbergia is most effective when grown with just one or two offshoots.

M. B. Foster

Billbergia pyramidalis, possibly the most commonly grow brmoeliad in the Florida gardens.

B. *macrocalyx* —- This is a tall, tubular plant, with leaves flaring towards the top. The leaves are a soft green, banded with white; the typical Billbergia-type inflorescence bears red bracts and frosted pinkish-white, blue-tipped flowers. Grows well in the ground or on trees.

B. *meyeri* — This Billbergia belongs to a group which includes B. *pallidiflora, B. porteana, B. rosea, B. venezuelana,* and B. *zebrina.* They differ in petal colors and leaf colors and the shape of the ovaries, but all have a pendent inflorescence. The petals curl back when the flowers open (one or two each day), leaving the stamens and pistil exposed. The following day the petals uncurl and straighten out. B. *meyeri* is a tall, thin, tube-like plant with gray-brown foliage that is heavily mottled with peltate scales. Its inflorescence of pink, lavender and yellow is attractive. As this Billbergia comes from dry, barren lands, it can withstand considerable neglect.

B. *minarum* — A rather rare Billbergia, but deserving of a place in everyone's collection. Its tall, narrow spotted leaves makes it an attractive pot plant specimen. The petals are of a peculiar gun-metal blue.

B. *nutans* — This is the friendship plant of southern California—found in almost every garden because it is easy to give a slip to a visiting friend. In no time at all it will form a large-sized clump. It will take either shade or sun and is grown in any medium. A potfull will last for years. The mostly narrow, sword-shaped leaves are 8 to 12 inches long, olive green but more red colored in the sun. The bracts are light pink and the flowers are blue and green on pendent stems. A highly decorative inflorescence, it is often used by flower arrangers. It is a winter bloomer. There is a miniature form of this Billbergia, both leaves and flowers being smaller than the type usually seen.

B. *pallidiflora* — This is an interesting robust Billbergia to be found growing in Mexico south to Nicaragua. It closely resembles B. *porteana* and B. *meyeri* in growth habit and appearance.

B. *porteana* — This is an old-time favorite, dating back to 1857. As can be noted from the colored illustration this is one of the most beautiful of all Billbergias. It is indeed a noble plant in size and structure. Its robust grey-green mottled leaves form a tall plant that reaches 36 inches in height. The pendent flower stem hangs over the side and the tips of the flowers often touch the ground. The bracts are a brilliant rose, wide-spread. The flower petals are green. It is a slow grower, but well worth waiting for.

Billbergia zebrina

Racine Foster

B. *pyramidalis* var. *pyramidalis* — This is probably the most commonly seen bromeliad in Florida and is to be found in almost every garden. Stiff, broad rich green leaves develop into huge clumps around the base of trees or against buildings, also on the heavy limbs of trees. The erect inflorescence rises to several inches above the leaves; the red flowers tipped with blue forming a most spectacular flower head. There is a winter-blooming and a summer-blooming variety of this Billbergia. B. *pyramidalis* var. *concolor* differs from the type plant in that its petals are entirely red. This particular Billbergia does not bloom readily in southern California, either indoors or out. Recently Mr. Foster introduced B. *pyramidalis* var. *striata,* a very handsome variation with light blue-green leaves striped with cream. As most variegated Billbergias are banded cross-wise, this vertical striping is both unusual and attractive.

B. *rosea* — This bromeliad from the island of Trindad is often found in European listings as well as in American collections. The gray, scurfy leaves form a narrow tube reaching to three feet. The pendent inflorescence has rosy bracts and yellow-green petals. It is very similar to B. *Porteana* and is often mistaken for it.

B. *venezuelana* — This Billbergia is certainly one of the most spectacular of all bromeliads. It is similar in habit to B. *porteana,* but its foliage is more strikingly mottled. It is a highly decorative plant whether in bloom or not and always attracts attention. The pink bracted pendent inflorescence may reach over two feet. The petals are chartreuse.

B. *vittata* was first described in 1848, but then suffered a variety of names. The true species has dark blue sepals which have an interesting little twist to them which makes the flowers truly distinctive. The leaves are greenish-brown; the inflorescence is somewhat drooping. Its suberect flowers arise from red bracts; petals are violet and green.

✵   ✵   ✵   ✵

SOME FAVORITE BILLBERGIA HYBRIDS

T HE ORIGINAL PURPOSE OF THIS PAPER was to present a descriptive list of the Billbergia hybrids most commonly found in cultivation in the United States. It did not take the writer long, however, to find this an impossible task, or at least one beyond her time and energy to pursue. No systematic attempt, it would seem, has ever been made to put these plants into any kind of order. Billbergias happen to be the one member of the Bromeliad family easy to hybridize and to propagate; hence, they have been crossed indiscriminately, with little endeavor being made to keep a record of the cross or to determine whether such a cross has been made previously. Many of us are growing hybrid Billbergias whose parents are unknown; in fact many Billbergias are sold in commercial establishments with no label of any kind. What these Billbergias are and where they came from no one knows. Not a few are attractive plants, worthy to be recognized and given an identifying name, but their background is a dark secret and probably will remain forever so.

Some Billbergias found in nurseries do have names, however; but, unfortunately, many of these are erroneous. For example, some of us have a Billbergia known as *B.* × *"Albertii."* Its origin is uncertain, and Mulford Foster insists that there is no such plant. Perhaps this Billbergia is a *distachia* cross, but we do not know. It is a stocky, broad-leaved tubular plant with dull green leaves suffused with light purple and creamy-white spots, then dusted over with a fine white powder. Regardless of its doubtful origin, this is an attractive Billbergia.

There are two hybrid Billbergias grown in Southern California gardens which have been favorites for many years. The one known as *B.* × *'Theodore L. Mead'* (so named by J. N. Giridlian who thought the plant should have some kind of appelation) was first distributed by E. O. Orpet of Santa Barbara who had received it from the hybridizer himself — Theodore L. Mead of Florida. No record was kept of its parentage. It is a lovely Billbergia — a luxuriant grower with low spreading soft green leaves and a drooping inflorescence with large rose bracts and green and blue flowers. A generous plant both as to flowers and to offshoots, this Billbergia is best when grown in a hanging basket and given a place where it can be enjoyed the year round, for the plant is seldom without flowers.

The other popular Billbergia hybrid is known simply as *B.* × *thyrsoidea.* *B. thyrsoidea* is a synonym for *B. pyramidalis,* and the parentage is very evident in this plant, as the inflorescence is upright and the leaves tend to form a rosette rather than a tube. The other parent is obviously *B. amoena.* This is a particularly attractive plant whether in bloom or not, for if grown in sufficient light, the leaves become a beautiful rosy bronze shade. In bloom, this Billbergia can hold its own with any other member of the Bromeliad family.

38

James N. Giridlian, of Oakhurst Gardens in Arcadia, California, has made a number of noteworthy Billbergia crosses. One of his first is *B.* × *'Elvenia Slosson'*, named in honor of a prominent garden club leader. This is an exceedingly graceful Billbergia, with very long, strap-shaped deep green leaves, which turn purplish bronze in the sun. The attractive inflorescence with its bright red bracts and deep purple flowers may measure from 24 to 36 inches. This Billbergia makes a handsome pot plant.

Photo by Padilla

B × *"Theodore L. Mead"*

B. × *'Thelma Darling Hodge'* is also a Giridlian cross, being named for a prominent bromeliad collector residing in California. This is a large urn-shaped plant, resembling *B. porteana* in size and shape. The long hanging flower stem bears rose bracts and yellowish green reflexed flowers. This is a handsome plant, which Mr. Giridlian considers the best of his hybrids. Another of his recent crosses, which is also very attractive, he has labeled simply *B.* × *'Violet Beauty.'* The striking blue-green foliage makes a fine foil for the rose bracts and large, wide open violet flowers. A clump of this Billbergia will have flowers throughout the year.

One of the most popular of Billbergia crosses was made several years ago by Mulford B. Foster. This is his *B.* × *'Fantasia,'* a beautiful cross between *B. saundersii* and *B. pyramidalis.* This hybrid very obviously combines the best of both parents and when well grown never fails to attract attention. The broad leaves prominently blotched with white, green, and rose make this an outstanding foliage plant and an inflorescence hardly seems necessary. However, when the arching spike with its scarlet bracts and blue tipped flowers appears, this Billbergia becomes even more beautiful, and all we can say is, "Thank you, Mr. Foster."

Another stunning Foster hybrid is *B.* × *'Muriel Waterman,'* named in honor of the late trustee from New Zealand. *B. horrida* var. *tigrina* crossed with *B. euphemia* var. *purpurea* made this lovely plant. It is a very striking Billbergia whether in flower or not, the rose-maroon leaves with silver grey bands and inflorescence of pink bracts and steel blue flowers making a delightful combination. Also worthy of note is *B.* × *'Henry Teuscher,'* named for the director of the Montreal Botanic Garden. It is a cross between *B. pyramidalis* and *B. venezuelana* and is a very robust plant resembling *B. pyramidalis* more than its other parent.

A number of Billbergia crosses have been made in Europe, but the only one that is easily procurable in this country is *B.* × *'windii'*, a cross between *B. decora* and *B. nutans* made in 1882. It is a very nice small plant with narrow, sword-shaped green leaves, tending to rose in good light, and a pretty nodding inflorescence with bright red bracts.

EARTH STARS AMONG THE BROMELIADS

Mulford B. Foster

Possibly because there is something very romantic about stars, whether they be in the heavens in their own galaxy, or whether they are commemorating some great event; whether they may be on the floor of the sea, or perhaps stars on the face of the earth such as our lovely star-like rosettes of the genus Cryptanthus, they are all romantic and should be universally acclaimed.

To suddenly come upon a carpet of leaf mulch studded with quaint star-like plants, i.e., a colony of cryptanthus species, is to feel the thrill of viewing a galaxy of stars, earth stars this time instead of celestial ones.

This could be your experience when searching through a semi-dry dwarf forest in the eastern part of Central Brazil. In our explorations there we found them in a range of localities, in shade and sun, in moist and dry areas, coastal and hinterland, principally in the states of Espirito Santo, Baia, Minas Gerais and Pernambuco in all shapes and sizes, banded and striped, variegated and solid colors . . . all intriguing and with an equal range of variety in color and form.

One has gaily colored leaves with stripes of pink, green and brown and crinkled edges as in *C. bivittatus.* Or we may chance upon *C. lacerdae,* very precise and symetrical, its lovely green pointed leaves with a bright silver band running down the center. So well designed in formal lines that they look "custom made."

Cryptanthus zonatus, however, with its asymmetrical shape and "permanent wave" leaf, carries the informal cross bands zoned in gray over brown and green. The leaves as well as the bands undulate with all the dazzle of a zebra racing across the veldt. Some will say that it is as beautiful as a snake, others are reminded of the pheasant's feathers, but almost universal is the feeling that this weirdly beautiful plant in your living room would start a conversation on any occasion.

The new species *C. fosterianus,* first described in this issue, is a sophisticated cousin of *C. zonatus.* Stiff, thick, formal leaves of deep magenta that are barred with precise though informal waves of contrasting gray bands, this new addition to the Earth Stars' galaxy stands out as one of the first magnitude.

As a stud plant this new species has been proven to have introduced the finest blood for hybrids yet found. In combination with some of the older species and in some of the unpublished ones as well, has been produced the most unusual set of unnamed hybrids that is to be seen in the entire family of bromeliads, for the leaf color range is not to be found in any other genus. In hybridizing we can make predictions by the stars!

And, these earth stars can shine right in your own home as they make ideal house plants, taking neglect and the shade or sun of a room, remarkably well. Their low stature very much finds an appropriate niche on a low table in the living quarters. Their long endurance under adverse conditions of neglect makes them truly an amazing plant. Although they lose some of their best coloration when they are asked to come inside and sit on a table for a few months, they never lose the design or pattern of their markings.

The lowly Cryptanthus earth stars have never reached the branches of the trees like their cousins the Tillandsias. They do not have the brilliant flower spikes of the Vriesias nor the giant stature of the *Puya Raimondii* but they deserve acclaim and certainly receive it as the lover of beauty in plants bows down his head to look upon their decorative beauty.

Botanically, the genus Cryptanthus was named by Klotzch, and was first published in the famous German Gartenzeitung in 1836. Analyzing the meaning of the parts of the word we find that *Crypt* means "hidden" and *anthus* means "flower" which indicates that the genus characteristic is that the flowers are inconspicuous.

Horticulturally, the earliest record of a Cryptanthus having been introduced into horticulture apparently was when Mrs. Arnold Harrison of Liverpool introduced *Cryptanthus undulatus* in 1827. Later in 1831 Mr. Sello introduced into cultivation *Cryptanthus bromelioides*. In 1859 *C. bivittatus* (the most popular today) was introduced at Kew Gardens and it first flowered there in 1861. This species has been sold commercially for many years as *C. rosea-picta* and to this day is known under that synonym. Then from 1855 until 1891 the most of the balance of the known species were found and introduced into horticulture. One of the most striking of all the species is *C. zonatus;* this has been commonly called *C. zebrina* in horticulture. It was first introduced by Mr. Quesnel from Pernambuco, Brasil, to the Paris Garden about 1842; it created quite a sensation when it was first exhibited and it has not lost any of its glamour to this date, one hundred and ten years later.

Mez, in his last monograph of the bromeliads (Das Pflanzenreich, 1935), recognized twelve species. At least eight of these species with four varieties are represented in the writer's collection.

In 1939 I found a new species called *Cryptanthus bahianus* in the state of Bahia, Brazil in the highlands, an area called caatinga which is similar to a mesquite. This was quite a surprise because practically all of the known cryptanthus species had been found in shaded, semi-dry locations. My next new species was *Cryptanthus maritimus*. This was quite different from the other known species as it has long grass-like leaves and was growing in wooded areas. My third new species was *C. pseudoscaposus*. This was growing on rocky ledges in moist, shaded conditions and has a character quite unlike any of the members of the genus for its flower head rises up from the leaf rosette on a thick scape-like member. My fourth new species was *C. incrassatus* and my fifth, discovered that same year, will be published in the near future.

41

In 1948 I discovered a few more members of this interesting genus, one of which is described, for the first time, in this issue, *C. fosterianus*. While this new species resembles, in its markings, the well-known *C. zonatus*, it is very easily distinguished, not only from its floral parts but by the deep magenta coloring and exceptionally long, thick succulent leaves. One of the first plants I brought back measured thirty-two inches from tip to tip of the leaves when it was fully matured. This species is distinguished by having the greatest number of seeds in each fruit; also the seeds are smaller than any of the other species I have examined with the exception of *C. schwackeanus*. The other extreme in seed size is in *C. beuckerii* the fruits of which contain but three or four seeds in each fruit. They are not only the largest seeds of any Cryptanthus but they are as large if not larger than any seeds in the entire family of Bromeliaceae.

In 1949 I first found that the flowers of a Cryptanthus are not all perfect flowers. The past descriptions of the genus have been "flores, hermaphroditi," in fact, all of the flowers in the bromeliad family are supposed to be such; perfect flowers with both male and female parts. When I first started hybridizing these interesting species I found that the little cluster of flowers in the center of the rosettes were practically always imperfect or male flowers and the flowers that appeared among the leaf bracts below the center cluster were perfect flowers; these generally appeared after all of the male flowers above had finished blooming. This meant that daily observations must be made both as to when the perfect flowers were in bloom and also the hour when the pistil was receptive to pollination. To date I have more than twenty successful hybrids in this genus; they make a most unusual array both in form and exquisite leaf coloring.

From the general appearance, a Cryptanthus plant seems to be rather distant in its family relationship from a Billbergia, yet, several bi-generic hybrids have been made by crossing those two genera. It is believed that the first bi-generic cross was made by Theodore L. Mead when he succeeded in hybridizing *C. beuckerii* with *Billbergia nutans*. Since that time the writer has crossed *C. bahianus* with *B. nutans*, also *C. maritimus* with *B. amoena*. Other attempts at crossing these two genera have not been very successful; this remains an open field for experimentation and it is hoped that we will find additional species which will cross successfully. Whether placed in first rank among groups of other plants in planter arrangements or as individual plant specimens, there is a great future for many of these new species and hybrids.

THE CULTIVATED GUZMANIAS

VICTORIA PADILLA

G UZMANIAS (NAMED IN HONOR OF A. GUZMAN, Spanish naturalist) are to be found growing chiefly in the Andean rain forests, although their range extends from southern Florida, the West Indies, Central America to western Brazil. These bromeliads are predominantly epiphytes, though a few species appear to have acquired a terrestrial habit. Guzmanias are not so numerous as Tillandsias and Vrieseas to which they are closely related, and it is perhaps for this reason that comparatively few have entered horticulture. During the past few years, however, a number of splendid species have been introduced, thanks largely to plant collectors looking for new material.

To Edward André — French botanist, horticulturist, landscape architect, writer, and plant explorer — must go most of the credit for introducing this beautiful group of plants into horticulture. He went through the most arduous and hazardous experiences to bring back from Colombia, Ecuador, and Venezuela specimens of bromeliads about which he wrote so enthusiastically. In his great monograph *Bromeliaceae Andreanae* (1889) he indicated that he had collected 122 species and 14 varieties of bromeliads, of which 91 were described as new. About 25 of these were Guzmanias. In André's time, however, confusion existed over nomenclature, and Guzmanias then went by many names: Caraguata, Sodiroa, Schlumbergera, Thecophyllum, Massangea, and Devellia.

In the September-October 1955 and January-February 1957 issues of the *Bromeliad Society Bulletin,* Mulford B. Foster and others give an excellent resume of this genus, so a complete description is not necessary here. It is sufficient to say for the benefit of the uninitiated that all Guzmanias have smooth edged leaves; that the leaves are usually glossy and form a many-leafed rosette: and that in most species (those that are not horizontally barred) delicatedly pencilled longitudinal lines in brown or maroon are discernible on the leaves, especially near the base. The flower head may be tall or may be sunken in the leaf rosette. Flowers are usually white or yellow; the scapes are often very brilliant, ranging from yellow to orange to flaming red and lasting in color for several months. Thus they make highly desirable decorative houseplants. For a complete key to this genus, the reader is referred to *Bromeliaceae of Colombia,* by Lyman B. Smith, Smithsonian Institution, Washington 25, D. C., 1957.

The cultural requirements of Guzmanias are similar to those of Vrieseas. As they come from the tropical rain forests, they need plenty of humidity and warm air. They do better in shaded areas. They multiply readily by offshoot and are reliable bloomers. In fact, they are very satisfactory plants to grow, responding gratefully to tender loving care and putting out blooms that are among the most beautiful and exciting in the entire family.

The following Guzmanias are those which the author has personally seen in collections or noted in American catalogues. There are many more varieties available to those who desire to seek them out, for in a listing just received from Marcel Lecoufle of France, several rare varieties were offered, as was also the case in the bromeliad catalogue of the Jungle Bromeliadium, of Bilpin, N. S. W., Australia.

G. angustifolia (narrow-leaved). This Guzmania, one of the smallest of the genus, was introduced by the collector Kalbrayer, who found it on the banks of the Rio Dagua at a 4000-foot elevation in the Andes of Colombia. It may also be found growing in the mountains of Costa Rica, Panama, and Ecuador. It has not yet been listed in commerical catalogues, being found chiefly in the greenhouses of those who import their plants directly from collectors. It is a dainty plant, its leaves measuring but 6 inches in length and 1/4 inch in width. There are two forms of this Guzmania to be found: the red leaved and the green leaved. The red form, however, tends to turn green in cultivation. The yellow flowers are borne on a dense spike about 5 inches long; the bracts are an intense red. For many, this is not an easy Guzmania to grow, but it is truly a little gem and worth the effort of nurturing it along.

G. berteroniana (Named after Carlo Bertero, who first collected it in 1818.) To see this bromeliad at its best, one should visit "El Yunque" in Puerto Rico, where at the height of its blooming season this handsome Guzmania may be found by the hundreds brightening the trees like so many lighted candles. It is to be found only on this island. From a medium-sized dense rosette of plain green leaves, arises a glowing vermillion poker-shaped inflorescence, about 9 inches in height, from which appears yellow flowers. It is not difficult to grow. (See *Bromeliad Society Bulletin,* Vol. V, No. 6, p. 70).

G. danielii Found in the rain forests of Colombia growing at an elevation of 5000 feet. This great Guzmania had long been a legend among bromeliad collectors until one intrepid member of the Society decided to go and look for it in 1960. It is really to Mr. Ralph Davis of Miami Beach that we, in the United States, owe the introduction of this glorious plant into cultivation. *G. danielii* is one of the giants of the genus, its reddish green leaves measuring almost 36 inches in length and its flower spike, 20 inches in height. Mulford Foster has described it as follows: "It was breath-taking, and unless one could actually see *G. danielii* growing high up in a tree in a mountain rain forest, it would be almost impossible to believe that it could live in such a location. Its giant quarter-inch thick roots clung so tenaciously and securely to the tree that it could only be wrested from its lofty perch even by the use of a good sharp machete."

G. dissitiflora (remotely or loosely flowered). This is another charming pigmy which has found its way into the greenhouses of those who order plants from their source. It was listed by André as *Sodiroa dissitiflora,* who found it in the south-western mountains of Colombia at an elevation of about 3000 feet. It is also found in the mountains of Central America. Its leaves are pale green, measuring about 6 inches in length and about 1/4 inch in width. The inflorescence reaches about 9 inches. The bracts are red; flowers are yellow. (See illustration). **Easy to grow and flower.**

G. fuerstenbergiana. This plant from the Andes of Ecuador is attractive whether in bloom or not, as its 12-inch leaves are vividly striped with deep maroon, which

Guzmania lindenii

makes it highly decorative.　　Whitish flowers appear from a bright red cylindrical spike about 3 inches long.　Rare.

G. gloriosa. This Guzmania, so aptly named, was first described by André who found it growing in the dry, sandy regions of the Andes in Ecuador at an altitude of approximately 6000 feet. Definitely not a plant for the small greenhouse, it is comparable in size to *G. danielii.* Usually it measures approximately three feet in height and in diameter, although Mulford Foster describes seeing this species just under five feet. When in bloom, this Guzmania is nothing short of breath-taking, its vivid bracts arising from a thick rosette of glabrous green leaves making it exceedingly ornamental. Unfortunately, the plant is rare and has not been listed in the trade. (See *Bromeliad Society Bulletin,* Vol. V, p. 67, and Vol. XI, p. 20.)

V. lindenii. Although this handsome Guzmania was collected in northern Peru in 1878, it has only recently been introduced into the American trade, thanks largely to the efforts of Mr. Lee Moore. As shown by the illustration, it is of great size, although unlike the other giants *(G. danielii* and *G. gloriosa)* it is found growing on the ground. Its leaves, measuring over two feet in length and 3 inches in width, are bizarrely marked with transverse, wavy lines, green above, red beneath. The flowers are whitish on a many-flowered, tall narrow panicle. Though the inflorescence is not outstanding, the foliage is so beautiful as to make this plant one of the most sought-after bromeliads.

Guzmania musaica

G. lingulata (tongue-shaped). When one thinks of a Guzmania, he probably envisions this particular species, for it or one of its many varieties is most often seen in cultivation and is also one of the common bromeliads to be found in the forests of the West Indies to Guiana, Colombia, Brazil and Bolivia. Dr. Lyman B. Smith also lists it as growing in Brazil. This would appear to be a variable plant. The writer has three that are labled *G. lingulata:* one has a vivid red inflorescence with long leaves; one has a rose inflorescence and tends to be stocky; and one has an orange inflorescence with many medium-sized leaves. In 1960 Dr. Smith, in order to make some order out of the confusion that existed with regard to this bromeliad, gave it five varietal names: *G. lingulata* var. *lingulata, G. lingulata* var. *splendens. G. lingulata* var. *cardinalis. G. lingulata* var. *minor* and *G. lingulata* var *flammea.*

G. lingulata var. *lingulata,* the type plant, is medium sized with smooth green leaves to 1½ feet in length. From the cup emerges the stunning inflorescence which may reach a foot above the plant. This appears as a star-shaped head of brilliant crimson bracts that last for weeks though the small yellow-white flowers are of short duration.

G. lingulata var. splendens. This is the red-leaved form that was formerly known as *G. peackockii.* This handsome plant, measuring some two feet in diameter, has under leaves of bright purple-red and upper leaves of reddish green. From the rosette emerges the inflorescence that terminates in a funnel-shaped purple-red flower-head. The small bracts in the center of this cluster are yellowish and tipped with white. (Replaces *G. splendens)*

G. lingulata var. cardinalis. This is considered by most growers to be the handsomest of the varieties of this species. It is a native of the western Andes of Colombia where it was discovered by Andre, who brought back seeds with him to Europe flowering them in his greenhouse, where the brilliant inflorescence captivated all who saw the plants. It is definitely a larger, more brilliant plant than *G. lingulata* var. *lingulata,* although it would appear to resemble it in every other way. It stays in color for many months. (Replaces *G. cardinalis)*

G. lingulata var. *minor* found from Nicaragua to Bahia is a relatively small plant,

Nidularium innocentii var. *striatum*

Nidularium fulgens

Neoregelia × *"Fairy Paint"*

Tillandsia punctulata

Neoregelia carolinae
hybrid

Vriesea × *"Polonia"*

Vriesea hybrids

Vriesea hybrids

Vriesea × "Mariae"

Vriesea regina

measuring not over 12 inches in diameter. The pale apple-green leaves finely penciled with purple lines form a small formal rosette. The inflorescence which appears at the end of a short, stout little stem appears as a raised cup of scarlet bracts and whitish-yellow flowers. The bracts may vary in coloring, sometimes being yellow or orange. (Replaces *G. minor*)

G. lingulata var. *flammea.* The little Guzmania from Colombia is similar in every way to the type except that the red bracts of the inflorescence are white tipped. (Replaces *G. minor* var. *flammea*)

G. monostachya. This plant may be found growing in southern Florida all the way down to Brazil. From a medium-sized formal dense rosette of delicate, bright green leaves emerges one of the most fantastic of inflorescences. On a stiff poker-like spike white flowers emerge from green bracts that are stenciled with maroon lines until they reach the tip which appears to burst into flame, so brilliant is its coloring. When this writer visited the botanical gardens in Munich and Frankfurt, this was by far the most exciting bromeliad then in flower. The Europeans who call this plant, *G. tricolor,* probably have a superior clone of this Guzmania, for it would appear to be far better than any of those collected in the tropics. Unfortunately, the coloring of this bromeliad is variable, for the tip of the inflorescence instead of being a fiery crimson may be a soft orange or even white. In the Everglades of Florida a handsome variegated variety of this Guzmania has been discovered. The inflorescence of this plant lasts but a short time — hence its lack of popularity. André found it growing in the warm regions of Venezuela, Colombia, and Ecuador at an elevation of 3000 feet.

G. musaica (variegated). This is truly one of the most elegant and beautiful of all bromeliads. It was discovered in 1867 near Ocana, Colombia, at a 3000-foot elevation by Gustav Wallis, who sent it on to the chief editor of the French journal *L'Illustration Horticole* for identification. He and his co-worker, André described the plant as a Tillandsia, but in the next few years it was transferred into Billbergia, Caraguata, Massangea, and Vriesea. Finally, in 1896, Mez placed it in Guzmania where it has rightfully remained. According to Albert Bruchmueller, who collected the plant in 1873, the old plant produces "below the stem a stolon 10 to 12 inches long on which the roots and leaves form, the roots taking hold of the first tree they can reach. The flower spike is 12 to 15 inches tall, of a flesh color, changing to a brilliant scarlet as it reaches maturity. The flowers are close together, white and thick, like wax, from an inch to an inch and a half long, about 20 to 25 flowers forming a bullet-shaped inflorescence which stands upright on the spike. In places where this plant grows moisture is abundant during the whole year, but I observed that they grow more vigorously where well aired than in the thick forests. It is only found in one small district at an elevation of 5000 feet, and as it is a scrambling plant, the trees and plants are covered with it from top to bottom. Some of the plants, when not within reach of a tree to climb upon, have five or six shoots or branches, forming quite a clump, and I noticed that they do quite as well this way, growing in a kind of leaf-mold to an enormous size, the leaves being four inches broad and 18 to 24 inches long." As a foliage plant this Guzmania is incomparable, and when well grown (which is a difficult feat) it can assume noble proportions.

The bright green leaves are transversely banded very irregularly with dark green wavy lines much like illegible writing. This Guzmania apparently is variable in its coloring, as Bruchmuller noted that some of the plants were light green and darkly variegated while others were of a brownish color. A form of this Guzmania was found in Panama in 1946 by Paul H. Allen, collector for Missouri Botanical Garden. This is similar in appearance to *Viesea splendens* in its zebra-like markings and so has been called *G. musaica* var. *zebrina*.

G. nicaraguensis. Found in Guatemala, and Nicaragua. This is a medium-sized plant with thin, longitudinal red stripes against the smooth green leaves. A red cone of bracts forms first in the heart of the rosette from which the spike breaks. Rare and lovely.

G. sanguinea (blood-red) This handsome, unique bromeliad was discovered by André in the western Cordilleras of the Andes in Colombia in 1876. He was able to bring back living plants with him to Europe, this Guzmania blooming for the first time in his home in 1883. André describes the foliage as a "tender green tinted with red, gradually becoming in the earlier stages of growth spotted with violet-red, which, changing later on to blood-red, increases in intensity as the flowering time approaches. The coloration varies in different plants to the extent that some are entirely purple while others are more or less spotted." The plant is of moderate size, rarely exceeding 15 inches in diameter; the leaves measure about an inch at their base and are of a firm texture. The flowers are not showy, being of a pale straw color. There are two varieties of this species: one, in which the flowers remain deep in the heart, and the other, *G. sanguinea* var. *erecta,* in which the flower head rises above the leaves. Most certainly this is a Guzmania which should be in everyone's collection, for when the plant starts to color, just prior to blooming, it is a sight to behold. Another distinguishing characteristic of this Guzmania is that the offshoots appear in the center, as in the case of *V. splendens.* Also found growing in dense forests on trees on Cocos Island of Costa Rica, Trinidad, and Ecuador.

G. vittata (striped). Although the discovery of this Guzmania dates from 1830, it has only recently been introduced into the United States. It was found growing in Colombia and along the Amazon by Lee Moore, who has been successful in sending back live specimens. It is a smallish plant with narrow leaves with pointed ends, that are of a soft green bizarrely barred with purple banding on the undersides. The inflorescence is lacking in interest, being a tall, green spike, terminating in a small, round head of greenish bracts, edged with deep purple. Flowers are white. This little plant is highly decorative, for its soft feather-like foliage resembles the plumage of a tropical bird.

G. zahnii. This exquisite bromeliad, discovered by the explorer Zahn in the Chiriqui Mountains of Central America, has long been popular with collectors. It is certainly one of the daintiest of all bromeliads, for its slender leaves, although attaining a length of 20 inches, have a semi-transparent, delicate grace not to be found in other members of this plant family. It is a plant of very brilliant coloring, and as a foliage plant alone occupies a high rank. The numerous soft green leaves are conspicuously striped vertically with red-brown or crimson on both sides. Sometimes, if given enough light, the leaves will become coppery in tone with tinges of pink at the ends of the leaves. Just prior to blooming, the whole heart assumes a roseatte hue. The flower-spike is almost as long as the leaves; the bracts are bright red and the flowers are yellow. Remains in color for many months.

NEOREGELIA SPECIES MOST COMMONLY FOUND IN CULTIVATION

VICTORIA PADILLA

F OR THE NOVICE JUST STARTING his collection of bromeliads, Neoregelias will prove to be one of the most rewarding of the genera to grow. First of all, Neoregelias are highly decorative plants and are a delight to the eye whether in bloom or not. Then they are easy to care for, tolerating almost any condition under which they are forced to grow. They are relatively robust, too, withstanding temperatures that would kill most other bromeliads. In mild climates they will flourish outdoors planted in the ground in semi-shaded areas; in less temperate regions, as they are primarily foliage plants, they make perfect house specimens. In crowded greenhouses they seem perfectly happy in any situation and will do well under benches where it is dark and damp. They are not fussy as to soil (any well drained compost will do) and they seem to thrive regardless of the alkalinity of the water. Some species prefer dense shade, but others require the optimum amount of light (just short of direct sunlight) to bring out their best color — here the grower will have to do a little experimenting.

Neoregelias are largely natives of eastern Brazil with a few species found in eastern Colombia and Peru. They have been in cultivation in Europe for a comparatively long period of time. Growing for the most part on the ground or the lower limbs of trees, they were easily found by the early plant collectors who brought them back to the Continent, where they have been popular house plants ever since. Originally known as Karatas, Regelia, or Aregelia (after the botanist C. von Regel) these plants were all classified as Neoregelia by Dr. Lyman B. Smith in an attempt to clarify the confusion regarding their nomenclature which had existed for many years.

For the most part Neoregelias are medium-sized, compact-growing, but they do vary in size from the tiny *N. Ampullacea* — an inch in width by 5 inches in height to *N. carcharodan,* which will attain a diameter of four feet. No bromeliad offers a wider variety of leaf texture and coloration. Some species have stiff leaves, armed with spines and covered with peltate scales; others are softer leaved and are outstanding for their glossy smooth texture. Some are just soft green; others are a rich maroon; some are a single color; others may be banded, spotted or marbled and red tipped. All Neoregelias have their flowers in a compound head nestled in the heart of the plant. Flowers are usually blue or white, but these are barely discernible when the cup is filled with water. The most spectacular Neoregelias are those whose heart turns a vivid rose or red when blooming time approaches — a coloring which usually lasts for many months and which makes these plants highly desirable.

At present, much hybridizing is being done with Neoreglias, with the unfortunate consequence that perhaps in a short time this genus will be as mixed up as are the Billbergias. No systematic procedure is being followed regarding nomenclature except in a few isolated cases. Mr. Mulford B. Foster was among the first to work with Neoregelias, and his crosses are among the finest to be seen, as are also those made by Mr. Julian Nally, of Gotha, Florida. Among the species most often seen in American culture are the following:

Photo M. B. Foster
Neoregelia farinosa, a fine plant having
the brilliant crimson cup center.

N. ampullacea —(1880) This is a true midget, measuring not more than an inch in diameter and five inches in height. Unlike most other members of the genus, this Neoregelia is stoloniferus, so it can be used effectively for covering hanging baskets, for climbing a pole, or for growing along a branch of a tree. There appears to be two forms of this plant in cultivation. Both have fleckings and cross bands of burgandy maroon with blue flowers, but the variety known as *tigrina* seems to be the more vividly marked and is by far the more attractive.

N. bahiana — (1935) This is another tubular-type Neoregelia, this species reaching about a foot in height. There are two forms: *N. bahiana* var. *viridis,* which is completely green, and *N. bahiana* var. *bahiana,* the leaves of which are red on the upper surface.

N. carcharodon — (1889) So far as this author knows, this species is one of the largest and most robust of the entire genus. It is best suited for outdoor planting, as its heavy appearance does not lend itself to being a houseplant. The leaves are gray, with maroon specks above and maroon blotching underneath.

N. carolinae — (1857) One of the showiest of the genus, this plant has long been one of the most popular bromeliads. It was named for Caroline Morren, wife of the editor of *La Belgique Horticole*. The soft green leaves form a good-sized spreading rosette, the center of which becomes a brilliant shade of cerise, vermillion red, or pomegranate purple when the plant is about to bloom. The colors of the blushing heart will vary in intensity and hue even from the same group of seedlings. The flowers are violet-blue. *N. carolinae* var. *tricolor* was first described by Mulford Foster in this bulletin in 1953. The plant is distinguished by its ivory-white, lengthwise stripes of varying widths. When the plant begins to mature, it becomes lightly suffused with pink, which color deepens as it begins to flower, the heart becoming vividly hued. This plant makes an exceptionally fine subject for the home, for its color lasts the better part of the year. It suckers freely. *N. carolinae* var. *marechalii* is a selected European strain of *N. carolinae*. It is a little more compact in form and when grown in favorable light the entire plant will take on an attractive salmon-crimson shade.

N. concentrica — (first listed as *T. concentrica* in 1825) Known in Europe as *Nidularium acanthocrater* and *Neoregelia proserpinae*, this is a rather stocky plant with medium-sized pale green, thick hard leaves that are slightly flecked and that are bordered with black spines. The center turns a red-purple prior to blooming. Walter Richter has crossed this Neoregelia with *N. johanis* and has obtained a very attractive cross, which he has named *N.* × *'Vulcan.'*

N. cruenta — (1828) Although this plant has been offered in American catalogues, it is not too often seen in private collections. It is described as being an attractive plant; the leaves of the upright compact rosette are broad and are of a light straw color which contrasts with "the painted finger nail" tips and the red spines on the margin. This will take full sun in some areas.

N. eleutheropetela (1907) This species is to be found not only in Brazil, but in Colombia and Peru as well, where Mr. Lee Moore has collected it. It is described as being a well-formed green rosette, with a reddish tinge if grown in strong light. The center of the plant spreads open and turns a bright red when flowering time approaches.

N. farinosa — (1939) According to Mulford B. Foster this Neoregelia has long been known but only recently has it been introduced into horticulture. It is similar to *N. carolinae* but its leaves are darker hued and stubbier. This species has shiny, green, copper, and maroon leaves when grown in adequate light; indeed, it is one of the most attractive of the entire genus. When it approaches flowering, like *N. carolinae*, its whole heart becomes a vibrant "crimson cup," this magnificent display of color lasting for almost six months.

N. fosteriana — (1950) This Neoregelia discovered by Mr. Foster on one of his more recent trips to South America is a highly ornamental plant and is distinguishable by its lightly gray dusted bronze shaded leaves. The tips of the leaves are a burgundy red; the flowers are pale blue.

N. johannis — (1884) The leaves of this Neoregelia are broad and firm and rounded at the tips. The center is diffused a lavender-violet. A hardy species.

N. laevis — (1912) A smooth leaved, medium-sized plant. (See description given by Mrs. Adda Abendroth in this issue.)

N. marmorata hybrid — (1885) *N. marmorata* is seldom seen in cultivation; what passes for this species is a hybrid of *N. marmorata* and *N. spectabilis.* This plant has olive green leaves which are vividly blotched with maroon to give a most spectacular effect. Tips of the leaves are red; the flowers are lavender. To bring out its best coloring, this Neoregelia should be grown in strong light and in poor soil. This plant does not want coddling — it is a robust species.

N. mooreana — This delightful little plant is one of Lee Moore's recent introductions. It was originally known as *N. ossifragi,* but this name was changed by Dr. Smith. It is a unique Neoregelia in that its edges tend to curl, a feature which makes it most attractive. Leaves are light green, edged with brown spines. Flowers are white.

N. pauciflora — (1939) This plant is similar to *N. ampullaceae,* in size, shape, and habit of growth; but instead of having mahogany crossbands, it has mahogany freckles all over its little leaves. A rare and desirable little gem.

N. princeps var. *princeps* — (1884) "Princely" is a proper name for this attractive species. The leaves are a plain glaucous green and are broad and wide. When the plant reaches maturity, the inner leaves turn a vibrant orange-scarlet, which color remains for the better part of a year. The little flowers are a pretty violet-blue.

N. sarmentosa chlorosticta — (1870) is a small, brightly colored upright rosette. The olive-green leaves, splotched with maroon, are narrower than those of most *Neoregelias* and are very pointed. The leaves are silver banded beneath; the flowers are pale lavender.

N. spectabilis (1873) This is another Neoregelia that is aptly named, for it is a remarkable, showy plant and is a favorite of all those who see it. It is the original "fingernail plant," its tips being a bright cerise-red. The leaves, which are spineless and leathery and straplike, are of a metallic green with faint transverse whitish bands on the underside. The flowers are blue. This is a very popular plant, because it is also a robust plant and multiplies freely. Some of the plants seem to take on a rose shading. The best known of these varieties is a plant that has been sold as "Pinkie."

N. tristis — (1857) There is nothing sad about this gay little plant with its lively brownish-red mottlings. The underleaves are a scaly gray with lighter gray crossbars. The leaves are red tipped; the flowers are a light lavender.

N. zonata — (1950) This is a highly marked plant, being both banded and speckled. The leaves are olive green, markings are wine red, and the petals of the flowers are white, tipped with blue. It is a sturdy little plant, and like the others of its kind, the more light it is given, the brighter the coloration. This is a semi-dwarf species.

NIDULARIUM AND NEOREGELIA

Charles Chevalier

Conservateur honoraire au Jardin Botanique de Liège

It was in 1854 that Charles Lemaire created for *N. fulgens* Lem. the genus Nidularium of which the different species had until then been tossed back and forth between the genera Karatas and Bromelia. The name of Nidularium had been given because the flowers are situated between the leaves as in a nest.

The initiative of Ch. Lemaire having been criticized by several papers on bromeliads of that period, the learned French botanist maintained his opinion, but recognizing that there was ground for certain observations, he divided his new genus into two sections: in one he grouped the true Nidularium, such as *N. fulgens*, *N. purpureum*, etc., characterized by an inflorescence bearing dispersed flowers between the bracteal leaves. Next, he gave the name Regelia to species which, like *N. Meyendorffii* Reg. have the flowers grouped on a simple inflorescence in the center of the bracts, in a sort of nest, more or less deep.

But, when he invented the name of Regelia, Ch. Lemaire probably did not know that this word had already served to baptize certain plants of the family of Myrtaceae: *Regelia ciliata* Schau, etc. Horticulture had even taken over this name for the Palms, at the present time incorporated in the genus Verschaffeltia, of Wendland.

Since two different plants could not bear the same name, O. Kuntze, German botanist (1843-1907) changed Regelia into Aregelia, a denomination which was accepted by Mez in his authoritative monograph on the Bromeliaceae (1935). Recently, Dr. Lyman B. Smith, the noted American authority on bromeliads, expressed the opinion that the name Aregelia was faulty and substituted for it that of Neoregelia, which, at the present time, appears to have been adopted.

Charles Lemaire (1800-1871) who is referred to above, was a French botanist who lived for a long time in Belgium where he was for a time chief contributor to the "Jardinier Fleuriste" and "L'Illustration Horticole." He had the reputation of having a rather quick temper which was, so said his contemporaries, related to the spiny cactus. However that may be, he was a systematizer of great worth, a wise observer, gifted with a keen critical mind. The majority of the genera and species which he created, harshly debated at first, are revealed to be perfectly correct and, at the present time, are accepted by all the modern authors.

The Nidularium and Neoregelia are, in general, medium-sized plants, ornamental, with leaves green or colored, capable of holding in their cups a quantity of water, more or less important. The flowers, without being very brilliant, bring, nevertheless a note of clear color to the middle of the bracteal leaves, more or less numerous, which surround them. These occupy the center of the rosette of leaves and are decorated with tints of color, more or less vivid, varying with the species. These are the bracts, of long duration, which constitute the most ornamental part of the plant.

Among the number of Nidularium most cultivated, *N. X Chantrieri* André is the most esteemed. It is a beautiful hybrid obtained in 1895 by Chantrier of Mortefontaine, France by hybridization between *N. fulgens* and *N. Innocentii*. It is a very beautiful plant with lustrous green foliage punctuated by black above, intense violet below, with vermillion-red bracts. *N. Innocentii* Lem (*Karatas*

Innocentii Ant.) introduced from Brazil in 1855, has beautiful green leaves, tinged with reddish-brown, dark-red on the underside, softly and finely toothed, with brilliant orange-red bracts and white flowers.

As for *N. fulgens* Lem. (*Karatas fulgens* Ant. *Nidularium pictum* Hort.) equally well esteemed and introduced from Brazil in 1854, it is a dwarf plant with showy leaves, arched, tough and hard, indented, of a lively, brilliant green, spotted with dark green. The bracts are brilliant scarlet and the flowers violet, tinted with red.

Another interesting species (*N. rutilans* Morr. (*Karatas rutilans* Bak.) is a handsome plant with an utricular rosette at the base, long narrow leaves, almost free from indentation, [marginal spines] lively green, with the spots darker, and short, bright crimson bracts surrounding rose-salmon flowers.

There is also in cultivation *N. striatum* Hort. Bull. (*N. aureostriatum* Hort.) with soft green leaves, marked down the middle with wide longitudinal bands, pale yellow, as in *Dracaena fragrans Massangeana*. Is this beautiful plant a pure species or should it be considered as a striped form of one or another species not yet determined? It is possible, for the return to a green type is already manifested in European nurseries. This question has not yet been settled by bromeliad authorities. A certain confusion that we have called attention to in the *Journal de la Société Nationale d'Horticulture de France* (December, 1931) still exists on this subject. Let us add, however, that in his excellent brochure, "The Bromeliads of Brazil" (1943) Mulford B. Foster shows without comment, under the name of *N. innocentii* var., a photograph of a bromeliad which, manifestly, is our *N, striatum*.

The genus Neoregelia is, from the cultural point of view, more important than the Nidularium. The species most cultivated is certainly *Neoregelia Carolinae* L. B. Smith, known chiefly under the name of *Nidularium Meyendorfii* Regel. Introduced from Brazil in 1857, it possesses numerous synonyms, of which we shall point out only the principal ones: *Aregelia Carolinae* Mez., *Bromelia Carolinae* Beer, *Billbergia Carolinae* Hort. van Houtte, *Karatas Carolinae* Ant., *Nidularium Carolinae* Lem., *Nidularium Meyendorffii* Reg. (Color plate in l'Illustration Horticole of 1860).

This species is, at Ghent, the object of a very important culture in view of the production of young plants valued by florists for the decoration of apartments where they retain their freshness for a long time. It develops a short and dense rosette composed of a score of stiff, tough leaves, erect in young plants, length 25-35 cm., width 3-4 cm., brilliant clear green, uniform on both sides, finely toothed. Bracteal leaves are brilliant vivid red, and the flowers white with lilac at the tip.

Under the name *Nidularium Marechalii* Hort. Makoy (*Regelia Marechalii* Lindm.), there is cultivated on a large scale, also in Ghent, a plant, the origin of which is obscure, even though it had been put into commerce by Jacob Makoy of Liège. We believe it to be only a variety of *Neoregelia Carolinae* from which it differs only in that its stem is shorter, its leaves shorter and broader and by the rose coloration of its bracts.

Neoregelia Carolinae and its variety *Marechalii* have been found to be easily modified, and from them have come, through various horticulturists of Ghent, different variations, not so manifest in the form of the leaves, but more particularly in the number, the coloration and the disposition of the bracts. These bracts are usually three or four, sometimes five, in number, among the seedlings they are generally more numerous: six or eight, sometimes ten, their color varies from pale rose to dark red in passing through the whole gamut of intermediate shades, even going sometimes to vermillion and dark violet.

A very important variation was the appearance of a central longitudinal striping. In *Neo. Carolinae*, it is known at Ghent under the name of *Nidularium Meyendorffii folis variegatis;* it was obtained by M. A. Gyselinck, a horticulturist of Meirelbeke, and shows its leaves ornamented by a wide, central band, clear yellow, passing to white towards the extremities; the bracts are red, shading to rose. *N. Marechalii* has given *N. Marechalii tricolor;* this form obtained by M. Declercq van Ghysegem, of Ledeberg, presents the same striping, but the yellow is darker and the bracts are tinted with bright red.

If *Neoregelia Carolinae* is the most important species of the genus, the other species merit equal consideration by horticulturists. For example: *Neo. princeps* L. B. Smith (*Aregelia princeps* Mez, *Nidularium princeps* Morr., *Karatas princeps* Bak.), a plant with short wide leaves, glaucous green, pruinose on the under side, and with short bracts, wide and showy, bright rose with violet flowers.

Neo. concentrica L. B. Smith (*Aregelia concentrica* Mez, *Nidularium acanthocrater* Morr., *Karatas acanthocrater* Bak.,) is a strong, thick-set plant with a tight rosette of broad, tough leaves, bordered with black spines, pale green, spotted, chiefly in the young plants, with dark brown, almost black, the reverse side being streaked with silver-grey. The bracteal leaves, successively shorter, take on, in the center, a pale, yellowish tint, strongly shaded with rose and violet.

Two varieties are distinguished: *Proserpinae* differs little from the type, with yellowish-white bracts tinted with violet; *Plutonis* has dark violet bracts and leaves less broad.

With this latter species one can compare *Neo. coriacea* L. B. Smith, but it differs from it by its dark green leaves, more or less tinted with violet-hued purple, and by its dark metallic violet bracts. We note also *Neo. marmorata* L. B. Smith (*Aregelia marmorata* Mez), a beautiful species with large, pale green leaves, marked on both sides with large, confluent reddish-brown spots, bright red at the tip. In order that the color of the leaves may attain its full intensity, the plants must be cultivated in poor soil, or better, on logs suspended from the roof of the glasshouse. *Neo. spectabilis* L. B. Smith has upright leaves, narrow, almost spineless, of a lively green with a spot of carmine at the tips and some transverse whitish bands on the underside. The bracteal leaves are not colored and the plant does not demand the lighting to be as bright as for the preceding varieties.

Other species are still cultivated under the names of *Aregelia* (*Nidularium*) *Binctii* Mez, *Areg. Makoyana* Mez, (*Nidularium sanguinarium* Hort.) etc., but they are chiefly collectors' items, which, although interesting, are met with rarely in commerce. There are also some hybrids, notably, *N. X Chantrierii* André, already described, and also those obtained by M. L. Dutrie under the names of *Aregelia amabilis* 1939 (*Marechalii X concentrica*), a medium-sized plant with short, broad leaves; *A. X. decora* (*concentrica X princeps*), broad leaves, green, with darker spots, rose bracts. It won a certificate of the first class with congratulations at the Meeting of Ghent (July, 1939).

Grateful thanks go to Frank H. Overton who translated this from the French magazine, *Revue Horticole*, Sept.-Oct. 1953

MY FAVORITE NIDULARIUMS

VICTORIA PADILLA

Author

Nidularium billbergioides

EVER SINCE I STARTED COLLECTING BROMELIADS twenty years ago, Nidulariums have been my special pets. From the very beginning, they proved to be highly satistfactory plants in every way: they required no special coddling; they never got scale or were nipped by snails; they thrived in darkened areas—usually under the bench—where no other self-respecting bromeliad would grow; they were not fussy as to soil; and they were hardy enough to be grown outdoors in planters or under trees. Despite all the neglect and unkind treatment my Nidulariums have received, they have always been handsome plants, have been dependable bloomers, and have rewarded me with many offshoots.

Nidulariums, probably for these reasons, have long been favorites in Europe, and the American will notice many lovely hybrids in florists' windows. These bromeliads, growing in their native habitat close to the ground on old trunks or stumps, were easy to collect, and so were among the first bromeliads introduced into cultivation.

The genus is not a large one; there are only about thirty species, all being endemic to Brazil; but much has been done in the way of hybridizing and a large portion of the two dozen or so varieties listed in catalogues are hybrids of European orIgion. Nidulariums are characterized by their collar or rosette which forms in the heart of the plant just prior to blooming. The inner cluster of foliage usually turns a brilliant rose, cerise, red, or maroon, and stays in color for many months. Unlike the blushing heart of the Neoregelia, in which all the leaves become suffused with color, the brilliant shading in the Nidularium is restricted to its collarette of leaves. The name Nidularium is taken from the Latin *nidus*, meaning nest, which refers to this formation of leaves.

The Nidularium is a handsome plant whether in bloom or not. It varies in size from a foot to three feet in diameter, but seldom exceeds one foot in height. The leaves are usually of soft texture, finely toothed, and vary in color from green to dark purple and may be plain, striped, or spotted. Nidulariums have rather large spines, but these are not stiff. Like the Neoregelia, the flowers appear deep in the center of the heart; in only a few instances does the inflorescence rise up from its nest. In most species the flowers, which range in color from red, white, and blue, do not open even though in full bloom.

Nidulariums are not difficult to grow if one keeps in mind that they like to be kept on the dark and damp side. For this reason, they are not too happy as house plants, where the atmosphere tends to be dry; but they can be brought into the home when they start to show color and brighten the coffee table for several months. They seem to thrive in any compost.

The following are some of the Nidulariums which I have growing and which I have found to be worthy of a place in any collection:

Nidularium innocentii (so called because of the white flower) and its several forms are old-time favorites. *N. innocentii* var. *wittmackianum* has plain green leaves. The inner cluster turns red at the tips, making a pleasing contrast to the white flowers. *N. innocentii* var. *lineatum* is a handsome bromeliad similar in all ways to the type plant except that the leaves are finely penciled with longitudinal striping in clear white. (see illustration) *N. innocentii* var. *striatum* is also similar, except that the leaves are more broadly striped lengthwise with yellow-ivory.

Two Nidulariums that are often confused are *N. amazonicum* and *N. purpurescens.* Both are large and showy plants, and their dark color makes them striking subjects when grown with plain green plants. The leaves of *N. amazonicum* are a deep metalic purple suffused with green. At blooming time the inner rosette turns a brick red—a startling contrast to the white flowers. There is a minature form of this, which I purchased abroad. This little gem seldom exceeds a foot in diameter. *N. purpurescens* has broad metallic green leaves suffused with purple and glossy purple beneath. The center bract is red tipped. The flowers are white.

N. regelioides was formerly known as *N. rutilans.* This attractive plant is popular because of its compact size, seldom measuring a foot and a half in diameter for me. The wide dark green leaves faintly spotted with a deeper green surround a rose rosette. Flowers are a deep orange. This plant has withstood temperatures to 32 degrees in my garden.

Nidularium fulgens (see illustration) always makes a perfect rosette of delicately spotted leaves, which with its prominently serrated leaves commands attention whether it is in color or not. The glossy light green leaves flecked with darker green spots is especially attractive in spring when dark blue, white edged flowers appear in the flower head of brilliant cerise bracts, which later turn pale lavender.

Nidularium billbergioides is outstanding for its flower head which appears on a long stem from six to eight inches above the center of the plant. Its flowers are white and the bracts are orange, while the leaves are a soft green. This is an attractive small plant. There is a form called *citrinum,* in which the secondary rosette is a bright yellow.

Nidularium × *'Francois Spae'* is a handsome large plant with broad green leaves which originated in Belgium. Its inner collarette of rose lasts in color for many months. There is a variegated form of this cross.

Nidularium splendens is the name of another bromeliad brought from Europe. Whether it is a cross or species, I do not know. But I do know that it is a very pretty rather slender green leaved plant with an attractive rose-colored inner rosette. It seldom is more than a foot or so in diameter but will attain a height of about a foot.

Nidularium × *'Casmir Morobe'* is one of the finest of all the hybrids. It is a large plant, a vigorous grower, and generous with offshoots. Its wide green leaves faintly dotted with darker spots make a handsome background for the handsome rosette of rich rose. It appears to be hardy here outdoors, its bright rosette lending color to an outdoor planting for many months. It lasts equally well in the house.

Nidularium × *'Mme. Robert Morobe'* is my most stunning cross. The leaves are two toned — the upper side being a lovely soft green, spotted with a deeper shade, while the underside is a rich purplish maroon. The leaves are prominantly toothed. When in bloom, the plant is a dazzler with its vibrant cerise collarette.

Nidularium burchelli is different from all the rest in that it likes to climb. The leaf rosettes are dull purple-red and grow up from the slender wire-like extensions of the base at intervals of every few inches. It has a dense flower head of orange-yellow. It can be grown either in a pot or on a raft or basket.

*   *   *   *

If you are in an area where the water is high in soluble salts, do not let your plants get as dry as you might if you were in a good water area. Water them when they are still slightly damp. A good way to tell if you might be having trouble with excessive salts is to look at the leaves. If the tips are brown and if there appears to be a whitish deposit on the plant, it might be that the water you are using contains too much salt. If you see a lot of white alkali deposited on the outside of the pot and around the inner rim and on the surface of the soil, it is obvious that your water is on the alkaline side. If so, then perhaps you have not been leaching your plants well enough or maybe you have been overfeeding a little too much and this has combined to give you too many salts for the bromeliad to tolerate.

THE PLEASING PORTEAS

Mulford B. Foster

Some of the plants that we now call Porteas have had a rather varied "name calling" career. Exclusively Brazilian there are only five recognized species and two varieties. Outstandingly decorative some of them should be much better known horticulturally, and since this is the one hundredth anniversary year of the genus, we feel it is fitting that plant fanciers become more familiar with its history.

The first plant to be called a Portea was found in Bahia, Brazil by Blanchet. It was botanically described by C. Koch in *Ind. Sem. Hort. Berol.* for 1856 and therein named *Portea Kermesiana.*

Photo by author

Portea leptantha Harms

The genus was named for Dr. Marius Porte of Paris for he was the first person to introduce this plant into cultivation in 1885. So far as we know there is now no living material under cultivation of this species and there seems to be no record of anyone having collected it again since Blanchet. Dr. Porte was a naturalist who lived in Brazil from 1834 to 1859 where he worked in the fields of paleontology, conchology, ethnology and botany; he also made an outstanding medical contribution in his humanitarian service during the cholera epidemic in Bahia, Brazil. (Biog. notes from Revue Hort. 1870 p. 230 by Houllet.)

To confuse the botanical history of the genus Portea a little more, we find that Gardner collected a plant in the state of Minas Geraes about 1840 but it must have laid in the herbarium, unnoticed, for forty-nine years, as it was not identified until 1889 at which time it was named *Portea Gardneri* Baker. Although this plant was, no doubt, the first Portea ever to be found, it was not the first to be named.

The Princes Sachsen-Coburg found this same species (of Gardner's collection) during their famous botanical expedition to Brazil in 1879. It was named and published (nine years before Gardner's specimen came to light) as *Aechmea Noettigii* Wawra in *Oesterr. Bot. Zeitschr.* XXX 1880. (Wawra was the botanist on the Sachsen-Coburg expedition.)

Later, in 1892, Baker renamed this plant as *Aechmea microthyrsa*; then, in the same year, reconsidered its validity and put it in another genus, naming it *Streptocalyx orthopoda.*

In the same year Carl Mez, in trying to clarify the confusions, renamed it

Portea petropolitana var. *petropolitana* (Warwa) Mez

again and placed it in the genus *Portea,* returning for the species name to that of Wawra, when he named it *Ae. Noettigii.* The Mez description of *Portea Noettigii* was published in *Martius Flora of Brazil* III. 3. (1892) 296.

But, this was not the final decision (!) Fifty-one years later, in 1943, it received its latest, and we hope its final name, of *Portea petropolitana* var. *noettigii* (Wawra) L. B. Smith because Dr. Smith considers it only a varietal form of the *Portea petropolitana.*

The original type species of *Portea petropolitana* (Wawra) Mez (first described by Wawra as *Aechmea petropolitana* in 1880) is now listed as *Portea petropolitana* var. *petropolitana* to indicate (according to the new nomenclatural rules) that it was the first one of this species to be named.

This species is now blooming profusely in the garden at the Bromelario in Orlando, Florida and is pictured in accompanying photo.

The author found this species in 1939 growing in the littoral within a few hundred feet of the Atlantic Ocean, in full sun and sand, in the state of Espirito Santo as well as in the interior.

It is a very robust plant. The stiff rosette of prominently spined leaves form a plant which often reaches from three to four feet in height when in bloom. The flower head is a rather compact, much-branched cylindrical panicle about twelve to eighteen inches long and continues to produce flowers from mid-October until January. The delicate white-lavender petals are held tightly in a cup of strongly spined sepals which are united at their bases and are barely distinct from the ovary. Sepals and ovary are a delicate pink-orange in color. This lovely combination holds a lavender pistil emerging just above the barely open tube of lingulate petals. Each petal holds two nectar scales at their base.

Unlike most bromeliads the old inflorescences do not decay and fall away after they have ceased to show any life, but, instead they persist for three and four years; they cannot be pulled out but must be cut off if removal is desired. However, they are not unattractive and actually make a dried arrangement in between the annual flowering periods. It is a lovely addition to any tropical garden.

Another variety is also most attractive. *Portea petropolitana* var. *extensa* L. B. Smith (see p. 88 this issue; also on cover of Brom. Bul. Vol. 1, No. 2, March-April, 1952) is perhaps the most graceful and delicate of all the Porteas. We first discovered it in a mangrove swamp area near the sea at Victoria in Espirito Santo, Brazil. It was growing in masses attached to the mangrove roots barely four feet above the high tide mark. The first plants we saw were not in flower and little did we realize what a beautiful bromeliad this was until we later found plants in flower growing on rocks near the inland bays of the littoral.

The light yellow-green leaves of this variety are not as stiff as those of the other Portea species and, although the leaf margin spines are large and jet black, they are really not very stout. With a charming open spray of flowers of lavender petals and apple green ovaries, this variety *extensa* is one of the most attractive additions to a bromeliad collection or garden that one could wish for.

Early in spring this plant brings forth a spray of delicate flower buds, each on a long pedicle that day by day continue to grow larger and more colorful. A month later the flowers, now ready to show their lavender petals, a few each day, continue to bloom for at least two months. Gradually the fruits enlarge and as they grow heavier the spray, now three feet high, nods gracefully above the narrow leaves and it remains a conversation piece until December when the berries will turn a dark purple. Rarely have they produced seeds unless they have been pollinated by hand or by the humming birds, although the fruits will be full size and solid whether it is with or without seeds. They have a pleasant sweet fruity odor and taste when crushed.

Portea leptantha Harms was discovered by B. Pickel in Pernambuco in 1929. Harms describes the color of the flower as brick red.

The author collected this species in 1948 in the states of Paraiba and Pernambuco; a fine specimen of this plant has been in flower the greater part of this past summer (1956) in our Florida garden. The petals are yellow and the ovary orange-yellow. So far as we can ascertain this species has never been in cultivation before. The plant reaches a height of four feet and as shown in the accompanying photo the inflorescence is corymbose (composed of clusters) and each cluster contains many flowers on small branches. The individual plants have eight to twelve lingulate (tongue shape) stiff leaves with spiny margins and a stout terminal spine. They were growing on rocks in large clusters in full sun.

Portea filifera L. B. Smith was discovered in Bahia by Racine and me in June 1939. This was the first Portea that we had ever seen, and, incidentally, it is the least attractive, from a decorative standpoint, of any of the species in the genus. The stiff, dark green leaves reach a length of three feet but the inflorescence which is subdense and cylindrical, contain many small flowers.

Portea Silveirae Mez was named for its discoverer A. A. da Silveira who found this species in Minas Gerais about 1900. The plant is a very rugged one similar to *P. petropolitana* var. *petropolitana*. The dense spike of flowers with reddish-lavender petals is a very decorative one and the writer took this species in both Espirito Santo as well as Minas Gerais in 1939 and 1940.

All of the species of Porteas bear their flowers on thin stems or pedicels and they have very small thin flower bracts at their bases but the colorful primary bracts at the base of each branch and all along the scape are quite ample.

T STANDS FOR TILLANDSIA

Victoria Padilla

Aside from comprising the largest group of bromeliads in the entire family, Till-andsias are also among the most fascinating. A collector could devote his efforts just to this one genus and find it a never-ending source of delight. Dr. Richard Oeser, of Kirchzarten, Germany, and Dr. Luigi Califano, of Naples, Italy, are two members who concentrate their interest on Tillandsias, and their collections are both exciting and beautiful.

Tillandsias are found growing natively from the southern tip of Virginia to five hundred miles south of Buenos Aires. This is the range of the ubiquitous Spanish Moss *(Tillandsia usneoides)*. Next in extent as to habitat is the moss ball *(Tillandsia recurvata)*, which will grow on practically anything it happens to light upon.

Tillandsias vary in size from a few inches, as in *T. recurvata* and *T. ionantha;* to *T. grandis*, which produces a flower stalk eleven feet tall. Although there are many Tillandsias which have smooth pale green leaves, the more common ones have grey leaves, which are lepidote or fuzzy like the common Spanish moss. No Tillandsia has spines on its leaves. Unlike other bromeliads the leaves of most Tillandsias do not form a cup in which water and nutriments may collect. Instead they are complete-ly covered with tiny sponges or peltate scales which retain water and absorb minerals from the air for food. The flowers are generally found in flattened spike formations and are either blue, lavender, pink, white, yellow or green. The bracts range in color from white and green to pink and red.

Tillandsias require little care, but they know what they want and will sulk unless given the conditions they need. They must have plenty of air—for naturally they grow high on trees—and so will not do well in the stuffy confines of a heated living room. As their roots are unimportant, they prefer being planted in osmunda, Hawaiian tree fern fiber, or similar material. They may be grown in pots, but if so, they must be firmly planted and have ample drainage. They will thrive attached to tree limbs (either living or dead), provided they are firmly fastened and the roots well wrapped in moss. They need a daily spraying of water and a monthly spraying of liquid fertilizer. Light, too, is a factor—for these bromeliads will often take the strongest sunlight in their native homes.

What Tillandsias should the beginner start with? His selection will depend, to a large extent, on his growing conditions, but no grower of bromeliads should be with-out *Tillandsia lindenii.* No other bromeliad ever introduced from the American tropics created the sensation as did this species when first shown in flower in Europe. None has been mentioned so often and praised so much, and none has been recommended so much for cultivation. This species is extremely variable. The most commonly seen variety, however, measures about fifteen inches in diameter with leaves pencilled in dark reddish-purple lines. The spike stands above the rosette on a round, slender stem before it widens, flattens, and takes on a vivid watermelon color. The flowers, which are usually a lovely cobalt blue, last for several days, and when they wither other flowers come out of the bracts, and this goes on for weeks. Even long after the last flowers have disappeared, the bracts remain in their brilliant colors much longer. The flowers will often vary in color and form. *T. lindenii var. regeliana* is a larger growing plant and one of the finest. The flower-stalk rises about two feet above the rosette. The flowers are of a very brilliant blue and are conspicuous for their bright white eyes. The writer has seen *T. lindenii* with single pink flowers, with double pink flowers, with double deep purple flowers, and with very pale lavender flowers.

Tillandsia dasylirifolia

Tillandsia filifolia

Tillandsia × *"Victoria"*

Tillandsia aëranthus

Tillandsia bulbosa

Tillandsia ionantha

Tillandsia cyanea

Tillandsia cyanea is similar in many respects to *T. lindenii,* its chief difference being that it is a smaller, more compact plant with a chubbier bract and usually more brilliant flowers. It is a true little gem. Mr. David Barry has crossed this Tillandsia with *T. lindenii,* getting an offspring which appears to have captured the best traits of both parents. It is called T. x "Emilie."

Another gem among Tillandsias is *T. ionantha,* a native of central Mexico and Yucatan. It is the elf of the genus, growing scarcely more than three or four inches in height. The leaves which are finely covered with gray scales are very short and pointed, forming a dense rosette. The flowers issue from the center of the leaves, peeping out very conspicuously and showing their bright blue-violet hue to every admirer. This little bromeliad is easily grown in pots and on the branches of trees. It appears to be quite hardy. As in the case of a number of Tillandsias this species turns a fire-red when it is about to bloom.

One of the most striking of all Tillandsias is *T. streptophylla,* also a native of Mexico. There are few species with leaves so twisted—in fact, it is almost octopus-like in form. The branched flower stalk, completely covered with gray scales, contains many lavender flowers which appear above the delicate pink bracts. This is an easy Tillandsia to grow and will thrive with little care.

A number of Tillandsias are found in their native habitat living on rocks. Such is *Tillandsia capitata,* a native to both Mexico and Cuba. Until its blooming time it resembles some of the common Tillandsias of Florida, such as *T. fasciculata* and *T. utriculata,* but when it begins to bloom, it is definitely unlike any other member of the genus. Its beautifully colored flower head is a combination of colors found in no other bromeliads—being a lovely symphony of pastels of gray, yellow, lavender, and brown.

Tillandsia flabellata is another outstanding beauty. Out of a dense rosette of leaves rises a two-foot inflorescence which branches out into spikes, numbering from four to eight, each long, narrowly-flat, and suffused with bright red.

There are so many Tillandsias for a beginner to try that it is difficult to list them; *T. Butzii, T. brachycaulos, T. Andrieuxii, T. bullosa, T. fasciculata* are among those which are charming and easy to grow. Such beauties as *T. imperalis* and *T. multicaulis,* which have lately entered the trade, need an experienced hand. It is recommended that the beginner get a collection of Florida native Tillandsias, which are easy to grow and yet are very beautiful. There are a number of Florida nurserymen who specialize in the native flora of their state and who sell these Tillandsias very inexpensively.

ALTHOUGH BROMELIADS ARE AMONG THE TOUGHEST of houseplants, those grown in the home or appartment need more light than most persons realize. In the northern part of the United States, usually any window with a screen or curtain gives adequate light during the summer months. In the winter, however, a window with a southern exposure and no screen is best. In the South, bromeliads may be given more shade. If your bromeliads can be put outside during the late spring, summer, and early fall, they will benefit. A lath house or a space under a tree with early morning sun is about right.

The decomposed plant   The fragrant inflorescence

Tillandsia decomposita Mez

This Tillandsia, lacking in the usual composure of most bromeliad urn-shaped forms, has been given its specific name because of this decomposed characteristic. It is a rootless plant surviving in Mato Grosso, Brazil, and neighboring countries to the south, by clinging with its corkscrew and wiry leaves to the tree branches. It continues to put out a succession of new leaves, each one taking the responsibility to curl and twist around a twig, the better to hold itself in the tree.

Year after year the plant continues its growth and sends its flower spike out from the center only to be pushed aside as the new continuous growth forms its twisted main body. In bloom, the flower stem is sometimes two feet in length, holding many exquisitely fragrant lavender flowers.

FRAGRANT TILLANDSIAS

Mulford B. Foster

There are, possibly, more species of Tillandsias carrying fragrance than those of any other genus in the Bromeliaceae, at least of the bromeliad species that bloom in the light-hours of the day. Tillandsias also have a habit of retaining their individual flowers over a much longer period of time than the majority of bromels. Few bromeliads retain their flowers in good condition more than twenty-four hours but many of the xerophytic Tillandsia species hold their blooms in good condition from three to five days, and it is some of these species, which retain their perfume, that we wish to mention in this paper.

Most of the outstanding odoriferous species are xerophytic in habitat, such as *T. decomposita*, *T. Duratii* X *T. tucumanensis*, *T. streptocarpa*, *T. crocata*,

64

T. xiphioides and, of course, *T. usneoides,* as well as others. Nearly all of them give off an exquisite scent every hour throughout the day as well as at night.

All of these species are at home in the southern countries of South America, such as Argentina, Paraguay, Bolivia, Uruguay and southern Brazil.

As to flowers, the above species have lavender or purple petals except *T. crocata* which has yellow petals, *T. usneoides* which has yellowish-green petals, and *T. xiphioides* which has chaste white petals.   Incidentally, these fragrant Tillandsias have flowers with spreading petals and do not have the close, tubular formed ones with narrow petals that overlap, as the majority of Tillandsias have.

Considering the plant contour, we observe that the majority of all the bromeliads are relatively symmetrically formal or well-composed in their shapes. However, a number of the fragrant species seem to be quite lacking in symmetry, or as the botanist would say they are

Tillandsia crocata growing on rocks in the state of Parana, southern Brazil.

"decomposed," being almost grotesque in form.   The best examples of this characteristic are *T. decomposita, T Duratii* and *T. tucamanensis* all of which have heavily lepidote (scaly) curled leaves and twisted stems making the plants attractively distinct in form. They have roots only during their early (juvenile) stages and later they hold fast to the tree branches by their tightly curled, clinging leaves.   Thus, they can adapt themselves to harsh, xerophytic conditions on scrubby shrubs or cacti and on rocks.   *T. usneoides,* for example, has been seen to hang from edges of palisades-like rocks (near Bogota, Colombia) in great sixty foot tresses, a phenomenon of adaptation as well as an example of the continuously self-elongating habit.

This Tillandsia is remarkable in more ways than one. It may surprise the objective observer who does not go around smelling of every flower he sees, that the commonest of all the Tillandsias, *T. usneoides* (Spanish Moss) disseminates from its single tiny and fragile greenish flower, one of the most elusive and delicate of fragrances between the hours of "first dark" and midnight. Perhaps only a few curious persons who, wandering under the Spanish Moss and experiencing this soft spring-night fragrance permeating the air on a March or April night, have traced it to its origin. In fact, the majority of folks are unaware that this fantastic bromeliad even "wears" a flower, much less one that "breathes" a perfume which any *parfumeur* would want to capture in a bottle.

Since this perfume is released only at night there is, undoubtedly, a night moth which, attracted by the sweet essence, gathers the nectar and inadvertently pollinates the flowers.

Although few enemies, outside of man, have been found which attack this Tillandsia, a tiny grey caterpillar, which resembles a section of the moss itself, has been observed on the moss; only the sharpest eye will detect it. Perhaps it is the mature moth of this caterpillar which seeks the night nectar when the fragrance is at its height.

There are, no doubt, many more fragrant Tillandsias than those we have mentioned, as well as species of other genera that offer a fragrance, so let's stick our nose a bit farther into this subject!

HOW TO RECOGNIZE A TILLANDSIA
Mulford B. Foster

The genus Tillandsia is the largest and most widespread of all the genera in the bromeliad family. More than four hundred species are known to be native throughout North and South America and nearly one third of them are native to North America.

The plants may vary in height from one half inch to twelve and fourteen feet; some are small rosettes, some are large urn-shaped plants, or they may be rather bulbous in form. The compact and rosette forms are generally small and often have twisted leaves. The flat leaf types which are generally smooth, if shade loving, or growing in moist, high locations, are usually the larger plants.

1. Tillandsia belongs in the subfamily Tillandsioideae; all of them have fruits composed of three carpels which are dry at maturity and burst open to release their seeds.

2. The seeds are narrowly cylindric with a plumose appendage which is straight at maturity. Seeds are carried by air as on a parachute.

3. The leaves are always entire (smooth edged), and are either glabrous (smooth) or lepidote (fuzzy). Most of the dry climate or tree-top species are covered with tomentose scales, whereas those in a moister climate have a smoother and broader leaf.

4. The petals are naked (no nectar scales at base) and are free (not joined to each other near base).

5. The flowers usually appear on one or more distichous (arranged in two rows) spikes but rarely simple (one row) or polystichous (many rows) and even one flowered as in *T. usneoides.*

6. In habitat most of the species are epiphytic but many of the larger species are terrestrial or saxicolous.

Many species of Tillandsias and Vriesias may appear to look so much alike that they could easily be confused. The one salient feature which is most evident and easily determined is the absence of nectar scales at the base of the petals of Tillandsias and the presence of such scales on the Vriesias.

The xerophytic Tillandsias, heavily covered with tomentose scales, are rarely confused with Vriesias. However, some of the more glabrous (smooth) and flat leaf types of Tillandsias may be confused with Vriesias if the petals are not examined.

V STANDS FOR VRIESEA

Victoria Padilla

Vrieseas are truly the aristocrats of the bromeliad family. For elegance of flower, nicety of form, and all-around beauty they are not to be surpassed. Even the tiniest of the species—little gems like *V. racinae,* for instance—have a certain distinctive air that makes them outstanding. It is probably for this reason that they have been so popular in Europe.

According to Mez, there are about 158 species of Vrieseas known, although many more have been discovered since his time. Some are plants measuring only a few inches, whereas others like *V. imperialis* are veritable giants, reaching a height of 5 to 6 feet and as much in diameter. The numerous whitish flowers of this species, it is interesting to note, exhale the perfume of jasmine, disproving the idea that bromeliads have no fragrance. The great number of Vrieseas, however, are average sized plants, seldom needing more than a four or five-inch pot. They can thus be comfortably housed in a small greenhouse or brought into the home when in bloom. They are at all times graceful plants, the leaves forming a perfect rosette.

Broadly speaking, Vrieseas may be divided into two groups—those with plain green leaves and those that have decoratively colored foliage. To even up the score for the lack of interest in the foliage, the plain leaved varieties have showy inflorescences, whereas those with mottled leaves have flower spikes of little interest and brilliance, the only exceptions being *V. splendens* and *V. guttata.*

Although the larger Vrieseas may be found growing on rock in full sun in their native habitat, nearly all of those which are under cultivation come from the dense jungle where they have much shade and moisture. It naturally follows that these plants when grown by man must have shade, warmth, and humidity. Vrieseas rank among the tenderest of bromeliads, demanding the protection of a greenhouse and constant care. They are rewarding plants to grow, however, for their foliage is always attractive and their inflorescence is a thing of beauty for many months. Most Vrieseas are generous with their offshoots—*V. x Marie* and *V. magnifica* sometimes having as many as a dozen pups. Thus if it seems that the initial price of some of these plants is high, in the long run they are inexpensive for one plant can be the start of a large family.

What plants should the collector start with? American nurserymen who handle bromeliads list most of the worth while botanicals and can offer the enthusiast a good beginning collection. For fancy hybrids, however, European growers have the best selection, as hybridization of this genus has been carried on in Europe for many years. No bromeliad collection should be without the following:

Vriesea carinata hybrid (x Marie) has almost no rivals when it comes to conspicuous and long inflorescence; its brilliant red and yellow flower spike being most appropriately called the "Painted Feather." This hybrid was made in Belgium many years ago and has been a popular house plant on the Continent.

Another plain leaved species is *V. ensiformis* also noteworthy for the parrotlike gayety of its inflorescence. Showy yellow flowers emerge from a bright red bracts rising from a rosette of leaves that are suffused a purplish-red at their base.

Vriesea x poelmannii, another plain leaved hybrid is outstanding for its drak red bract, from which come clear yellow, tubular flowers. It grows happily out of doors in the French Riviera.

Two Vrieseas that always attract attention at flower shows are *V. retroflexa* and *V. scalaris,* both pendant varieties. In both these plants the inflorescence droops below the pot to form a graceful curve. The bracts are a brilliant red with yellow flowers.

Another species which has a similar habit of growth is *V. magnifica,* known as the "Goldfish Vriesea." From the nice green rosette emerges an inflated spike that grows more or less horizontally and has the shape and color of a fat Japanese goldfish.

The most exotic appearing of all Vrieseas is *V. hieroglyphica,* long known as the "King" of all bromeliads. Fantastic purple-black hyeroglyphs are tattooed on both sides of its glossy green leaves, giving an effect so exceedingly beautiful as to almost defy description. It is not the easiest plant to grow, being fussy as to water conditions. As with this type of Vriesea, it is not remarkable for the brilliancy of flower or bract. The much-branched spike produces only pale green bracts and rusty yellow flowers.

Vriesea X *mariae* 'Painted Feather'

V. fenestralis is another distinctly ornamental foliage plant. It is a robust grower with foliage about 20 inches long and 3 to 4 inches broad, light green above and below, very densely marked with transverse streaks of deep green, profusely dotted with brown at the base and more sparingly at the tips. A similar plant is *V. gigantea,* the flower spike of which being similar to *Tillandsia utriculata.* Its pale-green leaves are streaked both lengthwise and crosswise with lines of deeper green, and in the checks thus formed the color is creamy-white.

V. saundersii or *V. botafogensis* is unquie as to coloring. Its fine broad short, elegantly recurving leaves, glaucous on the upper side, are slightly freckled with white, and densely dotted beneath with claret-purple. The scape is not showy, being of a glossy, pale yellow bearing flowers that are sulphur-yellow.

Vriesea guttata has dull blue-green leaves completely peppered with small maroon spots. A smallish plant, it is at all times intriguing, but especially when it is in bloom. Its inflated, over-lapping pink bracts are covered with a "talcum powder," and resemble something that might come from the sea. Although the pale yellow flowers are not spetacular, the bracts are outstandingly lovely.

Preeminent among Vrieseas is the all-time favorite *V. splendens*. Not too fussy about growing conditions, it is always a joy, especially when its sword-like inflorescence is in color. It is one of the most common bromeliads in cultivation as it is raised by the thousands from seed all over Europe. In Belgium it flowers within three years from seed. It is one of the showiest of all bromeliads, being well worth growing for its foliage alone. The gracefully recurved leaves, about 1 to 1½ feet long, 1 to 1½ inches broad, are thin and flexible, bright green above, marked with distinct-cross-bands of purlish black, especially beneath. The flower scape stands well above the foliage and retains its brightness for several months.

* * * *

VRIESEA SPLENDENS

Mulford B. Foster

There have been so many different names attached to *Vriesea splendens*, especially in horticulture, that it might be timely to attempt to unravel a bit of the confusion.

Vriesea splendens is now officially known under the three recognized varietal names:

1. *Vriesea splendens* var. *splendens*, the strikingly-banded phase.

2. *V. splendens* var. *longibracteata*, the all-green-no-bands phase which until recently was known under the species name of *V. longibracteata*.

3. *V. splendens* var. *striatifolia*, the phase with no bands, but with longitudinal white and green stripes. This variety was illustrated and described by the writer on p. 92 of Vol. V, 1955, of the Bromeliad Bulletin.

Commercially and horticulturally we see the following types listed:

a. *V. splendens* "Major", is a horticultural selected clone.

b. *V. splendens* "Flammendes Schwert" is a cross between *V. splendens* "Major" and *V. splendens* var. *longibracteata*.

c. *V. splendens* "Illustris" is a cross between *V. splendens* var. *splendens* and *V.* "Flammendes Schwert".

d. *V. splendens* X "Chantrieri" is another selected clone made between two phases of *V. splendens* var. *splendens*.

All of the above four phases are of horticultural origin. They are selected clones or crosses between clones or varieties.

Rt. 3, Box 658, Orlando, Fla

TERRESTRIAL BROMELIADS

MULFORD B. FOSTER

(A reprint by popular request of an article which appeared in the
Cactus and Succulent Journel.)

OF THE TERRESTRIAL types of bromeliads, Dyckias have been the best known among collectors. Horticulturally, they have been used, I believe, more than any other terrestrial bromeliad.

In the book, "Succulents for the Amateur" there is but one page devoted to the bromeliad family and on that page there are just three species mentioned, *Dyckia sulphurea*, *D. rariflora* and *Hechtia Texensis*. All three of these are worthwhile subjects and do very well in almost any succulent garden in the south of Florida or California and for indoor gardens, protected from severe freezing; they do well in pots.

Generally speaking, the Dyckias are not difficult subjects for the collector and do not require much pampering. Most of them enjoy a slightly acid or neutral soil and I have found that they are quite happy growing in a leaf-mold and sand mixture with pulverized dairy manure or any good organic fertilizer. They all enjoy full light conditions and while they are quite drought resistant they can take plenty of water when the drainage is good.

All of the Dyckias have stiff, spine-edged succulent leaves, most of the species having green leaves. The flowers range from sulphur yelow to brilliant orange and generally appear in the spring. Unlike their cousins, the pineapples, Dyckias always send their flower spike laterally from the side of the plant. The axis remains sterile and continues to grow year after year. The larger types often form a yucca-like trunk, but the smaller species cover the ground in mat formation.

Most of the Dyckias are native to Brazil but neighboring South American countries have a few species. They are generally found growing on or in the crevices of rocks.

In private collections the two most common Dyckias have been *D. sulphurea* and *D. rariflora*. The large botanical collections have had a few additional ones such as *D. multiflora, D. altissima, D. frigida, D. Montevidedensis* and *D. remotiflora.*

From my collecting in Brazil I have introduced to this country the following known species: *D. coccinea, D. minarum, D. microcalyx, D. leptostachys, D. sordida, D. ferruginea,* as well as three of my new discoveries, *D. simulans, D. ursina* and *D. Fosteriana,* plus several new hybrids. Of the earlier introductions from Eurpoe, the first two Dyckias, *(sulphurea* and *rariflora)* have been the only ones suitable for small collections because of their convenient size. However, from my own collecting, the *D. coccinea, D. minarum, D. leptostachys* and *D. simulans* are all of a small enough size to interest the succulent collector limited to pot culture.

Dyckia minarum is one of the smallest sized plants in the group. I have seen this plant which averages two to three inches in diameter growing in rather large beds. When in bloom, with its six to eight inch spikes of orange-yellow flowers, it is an interesting subject. The green leaves are stiff and the plant is rather compact.

Dyckia coccinea is quite a hardy plant and grows in much more compact masses than many Dyckias. When grown in the open the individual plants do not show up as

Author

Left center—*D. fosteriana* — Right center—*D. minarum*
D. ursina

distinctly as most Dyckias. The lepidote olive green leaves, four to seven inches long, are narrow with an upright growth; the red-orange flowers are on a tall, 18 inch spike, and they add a nice note of color in the early spring and summer. This species grows natively in open rocky fields and is exceptionally drought resistant.

Dyckia microcalyx is a medium sized plant but certainly the most floriferous Dyckia I have ever had. It produces from one to three tall branched flower stalks each year with hundreds of yellow flowers thereon; it makes an excellent outdoor rock garden subject. The mass of curved, narrow, heavy spined leaves is a real addition to any succulent collection.

Dyckia leptostachya has been at home in our garden from the moment of its arrival from Brazil where we found it on rocky slopes in far off Matto Grosso. It grows in sun or shade, but of course blooms best in full light. It has fewer leaves than most of the Dyckias. They vary from maroon to green and most of the plants have produced at least two spikes of flowers in succession each spring. It reproduces by shooting out underground stolons and new plants will continue to develop around the matured plants. The flowers, on an eighteen to twenty-four inch spike, are of a rich orange in color. I have seen solid mat beds of these Dyckias eight to ten feet in diameter.

D. ursina

Dyckia frigida, an early bloomer coming from February to June, withstands quite a cool climate and dry conditions in sun or shade. The plants are from twelve to eighteen inches in diameter and the branched flower spike, at least three feet high, carries a good supply of orange yellow flowers. The green leaves are glabrous.

Dyckia ursina is well named. The flower spike and even the sepals and part of the petals are covered with a brown wool an eighth of an inch thick resembling a bear's fur. It is a bit large for pot culture but as a rock garden plant it will stand extreme conditions. While I found it in the tropics it grew high in the Brazilian mountains of Minas Geraes and the cold, raw, windy morning convinced me that it had not grown the wool covering for naught. Also the mid-day sun in that area was so severe that I am sure the wool covering has still another purpose. The branched flower spike is often three to four feet high and the flower is a lovely orange almost covered with brown wool.

Dyckia Fosteriana, according to Lad Cutak of spiny "chatter" fame, is the gem of the genus. And indeed it is a priority plant for its spiral whorl of grey leaves appears to be made of platinum and its brilliant flowers of gold. As a pot plant it will have no rival within the Dyckia tribe. The plant is three to four inches in diameter.

My Dyckia hybrid "Lad Cutak" is the most vigorous grower and bloomer of any of the Dyckia family, and it exceeds in size either of its parents. Several more of my Dyckia hybrids, not yet described, will be worth while new comers.

HECHTIA

These spiny, Dyckia-like bromeliads are less well known than Dyckias, although they are almost all natives of our neighboring country, Mexico. There are four Hechtias in the United States and one in Guatemala.

In appearance the well-armed Hechtias resemble very closely the spiny Dyckias. In fact, most of them could not be distinguished from Dyckias except by the inflorescence. They generally grow in much greater masses than the Dyckia colonies that I have seen. Most of them are also highly xerophytic and enjoy extremes in heat as well as fairly low temperatures. While the Hechtias are of more interest to the succulent specialty collector, most of them are a bit too large for the collector who has little space. The flowers are generally borne on long branched spikes and for the most part are rather inconspicuous, being without showy colors.

The Hechtias have one interesting character which is unusual in the family of bromeliads. While the flowers are monecious, having both pistil and stamens, however, each species has what we might term masculine and feminine forms. In other words, in the male form the pistil is not fully developed enough to function. In years past in many of the species, because of the different vegetative appearance in the two forms, each sex was named as a separate species.

Many of the Hechtias could hardly be noted for showy beauty, but one outstanding exception is the lovely Mexican species, *H. capituliguera*. The stiff, spiny, succulent leaves of this plant when in full sun, radiate an almost transparent amber color and lend a beautiful note to the rock garden. This species as well at *H. stenopetala* are two Mexican species that should grace every southern garden.

The four Texas species, *H. scariosa, H. Ghiesbreghtii, H. glomerata* and *H. texensis,* are all deserving of a place in any succulent collection. I know of no plants that ask for less attention than many forms of these Hechtias.

While most Hechtias are moderate in size, ranging from about eighteen inches to twenty-five in the spread of the rosette, with a flower stalk from one to four feet high, I discovered, (in Mexico in 1935) a giant among the Hechtias. Its rosette spread is over five feet across and its flower stalk nearly eight feet high. This proved to be a new species, *H. melanocarpa* (recently described by Lyman B. Smith), with a peculiar characteristic.

It has a central inflorescence! All other Hechtias, Deuterocohnias and Dyckias that I am familiar with have a lateral inflorescence; several other genera have this characteristic and I wrote a paper on the subject of "Lateral Inflorescence in the Bromeliaceae" in the National Horticultural Magazine for January, 1945. While this article was on the press, the giant Hechtia which I had been growing in my garden since its collection ten years previous decided to produce its first bloom. And from the center axis of the plant, (which no self-respecting Hechtia should do) upsetting completely my statement that "the genera . . . regularly producing a lateral inflorescence . . . are confined (in Bromeliaceae) to Hechtia, Dyckia, Deuterocohnia and Encholirium."

Now for a trip back to Mexico to find more Hechtias which will prove or disprove that *H. melanocarpa* is the only exception.

In general, the spiny leaves of the Hechtias lend themselves fittingly to rocks and blend happily in association with cacti and other succulents, thereby adding one more interesting form to the desert garden.

ANANAS

MUCH BETTER KNOWN on the table than in the flower garden, and of course the best known of the terrestrial bromeliads, are the pineapples. The Indian name for pineapple in Brazil where it is native, is abacaxi (a-bäk-a-she). If it is a pineapple which is not edible, they may call it either "Gravata" or "Caraguata," these terms being used, mostly, for spiny plants that might be utilized for their fiber.

Gardens in the sub-tropics should have many more bromeliads and certainly more of the genus Ananas which are not only decorative but useful in being edible. Their great long lasting fruit makes a delightful decoration in the garden that can grow them. This pineapple fruit head rises out of the center of the spiny leaves on a strong stalk which holds the fruit proudly erect. The fruit is topped with a small rosette of leaves which form a miniature of the mother plant. And this "top" in turn if planted grows and becomes a mother plant which produces fruit, fulfilling its cycle of maturity.

Nature, in this instance, does not limit her means of reproduction to one method. She does not risk the chances of the top of the fruit being destroyed so the plant also sends out from the base suckers, which root and soon grow into another plant. In general, the other terrestrial bromeliads grow and reproduce very much like the pineapple. Most other forms in this family send off side shoots soon after the fruit matures and within one year or so the old matured sections gradually die.

Ananas ananasoides var. *nana,* the smallest pineapple in the world, is not edible. The fruit, from one to two inches long has the delicious pineapple fragrance, but is small and too hard to eat. It is useful, however, because the plant itself with its miniature, long lasting pineapple makes a delightful decorative feature in any collection. It is easily grown and much quicker to fruit than the common pineapple, *A. comosus* (sativus). I have planted the top of this dwarf pineapple and had the fruit the following year. The plant suckers readily and grows in interesting clusters with as little attention and care as almost any plant one could think of. In Florida it does well in poor sandy soil or in the well fed heavier soil sections of the garden. It is happy in shade or full sun. Its adaptability is its one great attribute carried over from its native habitat which is in the wild lands of the cooler sections of Brazil; being able to grow also in the cerrado (tired land), the areas where everything seems to fight for its existence, gives this little pineapple a high ratio of adaptability.

Ananas ananasoides, typical form, is about twice as large as the "nana" or dwarf form, but in the growth and habit it is quite similar to the miniature form. Its reddish bracts on the fruit stem which is topped with the colorful flower head followed by fruit make it an added sparkling note to any tropical garden.

Ananas bracteatus is not only a beautiful and decorative plant for the garden but it bears a very good eating fruit as well, and certainly requires little attention. The red fruit and brilliant red bracts on the fruit and stem remains on the plant for months. We found these growing wild in many sections of Brazil where they were always a source of food to the natives, but we never found them grown commercially. One reason for

Author

Ananas erectifolius

this is that they grow quite a large top and send out many off-shoots from the bottom of the fruit, so they would be awkward in shipping. The flavor is a little more tart than our familiar commercial pineapple. Its channeled leaves have been used for a very strong fibre.

We found a variety of this species growing wild in the state of Sao Paulo, Brazil, called *A. bracteatus* var. *albus* with a fruit which is a pale greenish white. This variety is not the best for eating because of its seeds but it is, nevertheless, interesting.

Ananas bracteatus var. *tricolor* is the most brilliantly colored and decorative of any of the varieties of the species. It grows larger and is much more spectacular when in fruit than the *Ananas cosmosus* (sativus) var. *tricolor,* which too is a colorful variety. This latter variety was a great favorite among horticulturists fifty or more years ago and was seen in almost every fine plant collection of this country and in Europe, but it has almost disappeared from horticulture, at least in this country

Somehow, in Brazil, it took on the name of *Ananas cochinchinensis.* We found a plant so labelled in the Jardim Botanico in Rio and wondered how this native Brazilian species ever received a name that associated itself with Cochin-China, a country thousands of miles from the native home of the Ananas.

Either of these two plants would be an adornment to any collection with its colors of green, white, yellow and red stripes but they are scarce and will be scarce for sometime due to its slowness of reproduction. There being such a small percentage of chlorophyll in the leaf the plant does not reproduce itself very rapidly, so it remains a rare and much prized specimen. Their fruits are quite as delicious as the species form in each variety.

PSEUDANANAS MACRODONTES

Here is a pineapple which is not exactly a pineapple, but acording to its name, Pseudananas, shows it to be a false pineapple. This species *macrodontes,* we found in central and southern Brazil growing both on the coast within sight of the Atlantic Ocean and then far back into the northwest in the great state of Matto Grosso.

This "false" pineapple does not sucker at the base as does the true pineapple, but it sends out long underground stolons.

It enjoys a partially shaded area in which its stiff barbed leaves eventually develop

M. Lecoufle

Decorative Ananas—"Victoria"

Author

Pseudananas sagenarius

into an almost impenetrable thicket. The leaves are generally much longer than those of the common pineapple.

The succulent flower head produces a mass of lavender flowers held above delicate pink bracts which remain long after the fruit is formed. Although its fruit has a nice flavor and is interesting, it is not grown commercially. The fruit can be easily distinguished from the other pineapples as it does not have the typical leafy pineapple top.

A BROMELIAD MISCELLANY

Victoria Padilla

Besides those bromeliads already listed in past issues, there are several others belonging to various genera which the beginner will want to include in his collection. All are interesting, some of them are extremely beautiful, and most of them are fairly easy to grow.

Probably the most unusual of the lot is *Acanthostachys strobilacea,* a true epiphyte. It is difficult to believe at first that this unusual plant is a member of the pineapple family, for its thin, drooping, terete leaves give it the appearance of a rhipsalis rather than a bromeliad. The only visible clue to its real identity lies in the pineapple appearance of its fruits which emerge near the tips of the leaves. The red bracts (one to one and a half inches in length) which encase yellow flowers seem to be always in color. When grown in a hanging basket, this plant can be made into a handsome specimen, its leaves attaining a length of about eighteen inches, forming a veritable cascade. The writter has found it hardy in Southern California, where it can also be grown attached to trees or placed in a rockery. It likes moisture, but apparently does not need too much care. It is interesting to note that it has been in horticulture since 1841, a long time so far as bromeliads are concerned.

Orthophytum navioides (formerly published in Cryptanthopsis) is one of the unique gems of the bromeliad family. It was discovered by Mulford Foster in one of his collecting trips in Brazil and although the genus Orthophytum had been found some years previous, this particular species proved to be a new one. This delightful plant with its radiant whorl of shiny leaves, which turn red when coming into flower is comparatively tiny, so would fit well in any collection. Its white flowers which form in its heart smell like Ivory soap! A colored illustration of this bromeliad is to be found in Foster's *Brazil. Orchid of the Topics.*

To see *Quesnelia arvensis* in bloom is to fall in love with it. A robust plant, it is not for the person who has a tiny, crowded greenhouse. In Southern California it grows happily outdoors in filtered light and will stand several degrees of frost. Its large cone-shaped flower head of watermelon pink stays in brilliant color for many months. A smaller Quesnelia with an equally stunning bloom is *Quesnelia testudo.* The leaves of this plant are of a soft green, whereas those of *Quesnelia arvensis* are heavier in texture and more prominently spined. Both plants are a little slow to flower, but once they have been established, their offshoots seem to flower at regular intervals. Both will take much abuse and do not seem to mind a little sun and even a light drought for they have received both in the writer's garden.

Another very beautiful bromeliad which always creates a sensation when in bloom is *Portea petropolitana var. extensa.* A large showy plant, endemic to Brazil, it is easily grown outdoors in the warmer areas of the South, where it is happy in a pot, on a tree, or attached to a piece of fir bark hung on a wall. It is a plant of upward growth, its pale green leaves being heavily spined. Although the plant is decorative whether or not in bloom, it is spectacular when in flower. It has a large loosely branched inflorescence of tubular flowers in pink, green, and lavender which lasts in color for months. It is definitely a "must" in every collection. It is not a fussy plant and will respond to whatever treatment is given it.

For those who have the room, *Hohenbergia stellata* is another plant that definitely should be considered. Its many broad light-green leaves form a large imposing rosette from which emerges an inflorescence that is truly exotic.

A NEW GENUS IN BROMELIACEAE

Julian Nally

FOSTERELLA   L. B. Smith, gen. nov.

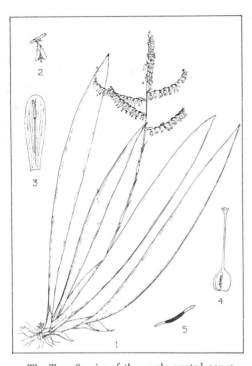

The Type Species of the newly created genus.
Fosterella micrantha (Lindl.)
L. B. Smith, comb. nov.

Some of us are fortunate in having an *Aechmea Fosteriana,* a *Canistrum Fosterianum, a Neoregelia Fosteriana,* a *Vriesea Fosteriana* in our collections, attractive evidence of the remarkable discoveries of Mulford B. Foster in the field of Bromeliaceae.

Now this specific name, which appears eighteen times in as many genera, receives the final accolade by becoming a new genus, Fosterella. This well-deserved tribute to the greatest discoverer of new species in the Bromeliaceae comes from Dr. Lyman B. Smith, who published in the May issue of *Phytologia* the reason for this realignment in the Pitcairniodeae.

When Dr. Smith was able to examine the type specimen of Cottendorfia, *Cottendorfia florida,* thanks to the loan of the material from Professor Merxmuller of Botanisches Staatssámlung of Munich, Germany, it was discovered that Lindmania unexpectedly consisted of two genera, one of which was not separable from Cottendorfia. In Dr. Smith's words, "Typical Lindmania, which is a native of the Guyana Highland of southern Venezuela, has the short basal placentae supposedly distinctive of Cottendorfia, and in addition shares with it the new character of versatile anthers. The remainder of Lindmania, which is found from Mexico to Argentina, has placentae extending most of the height of the locule and basified anthers. It constitutes a new genus . . . This new genus is dedicated to Mulford B. Foster, discoverer extraordinary of new species of Bromeliaceae."

Perhaps some will wonder why Lindmania could not be retained as a valid name since it has an honorable history extending back over more that a half century. The reason for dropping it completely is due to the fact that the type species has now been proven by Dr. Smith to be a Cottendorfia, so the generic name has no standing, leaving thirteen Lindmania orphans without a valid name of their own. This deficiency has been gracefully and graciously remedied by Dr. Smith, who gave them a haven under Fosterella.

Of the thirteen species in this new genus, six, a very high percentage, bear the specific name of a man, in most instances a man distinguished in the field of plant exploration.

Bromelia balansae

Cryptanthus

Hohenbergia stellata

*Portea
petropolitana
var. extensa*

*Acanthostachys
strobilaceae*

Vriesea splendens

Probably only two Fosterellas are to be found in collections. The more common (the term is used relatively) is *Fosterella penduliflora,* which is hardly distinguishable to the casual eye from the other, which is the type species, *Fosterella micrantha.* This latter species, which Mr. Foster has collected himself, is the only North American representative, having been taken in Oaxaca, Mexico, and also in Salvador. It is a delicately formed plant with many tiny white flowers. Though diminutive and not showy, the plant is an interesting adjunct to any bromeliad collection. It has been observed that the seeds have been known to self-sow themselves in adjoining pots when a plant has bloomed on a greenhouse bench.

A description of *Fosterella micrantha,* the type, is described as followed by Dr. Smith: Flowering plant 3-7 dm. high: leaves entire constricted above the sheath: blades lanceolate, acuminate, 30 cm. long, 4 cm. wide, thin, glabrous above, densely furaceous-lepidote below; scape slender and erect; scape-bracts lanceolate or lance-ovate, thin; inflorescence amply bipinnate, up to 26 cm. long, arachnoid; branches curved-ascending, many times longer than their subtending bracts; floral bracts ovate, acuminate, slightly longer than the pedicels; flowers secund and nutant; sepals triangular-ovate, obtuse, 3-4 mm. long; petals narrowly elliptic, obtuse, 7-9 mm. long; style slender, elongate; stamens distinctly shorter than the petals.

Gotha, Florida

Dyckia fosteriana, a silvered leafed gem growing in
large clusters and withstands frost and sun.

HOW TO DETERMINE THE CULTURE OF BROMELIADS FROM THEIR APPEARANCE

Walter Richter

Enthusiasm for bromeliads is gaining momentum everywhere. All over the world people are now growing these interesting plants, although, in many instances, they do not know how to give them the correct care and have trouble accordingly. It is not difficult, however, to provide the proper culture for bromeliads if one will study carefully the plants themselves.

Since the "Bulletin" is read in all parts of the globe, it is not possible to consider the growing conditions to be found in each country. Many of the hardy bromeliads can be grown out of doors in California and Florida, where many subtropical plants are raised; but in less favorable climates, these plants must be grown under glass. Here in my country, Germany, it is very difficult, and often impossible, to obtain a good coloring of the leaves with the sun-loving varieties because the intensity of the light is not sufficient. This article deals entirely with the care of bromeliads in the home or greenhouse. In an environment where conditions can be controlled, it is easy to grow bromeliads successfully.

Bromeliads differ from other plants in a number of ways. Most plants, depend upon water for their existence and have roots which absorb the water from the soil. This is not true with bromeliads. The root system of bromeliads is often insignificant and is used to attach the plant to branches, palms, or cacti, and the roots absorb water only to a certain degree. Most of the water which a bromeliad consumes is taken through cells at the base of the rosette—the so-called scales or hairs on the upper or lower side of the leaves. The cells at the base of the leaves are not visible, and one cannot form an opinion from them as to the needs of the particular plant. It is different, however, with scales. In many cases the appearance of the plant is determined by them. The best example of the decorative value of scales is *Achmea fasciata,* with its silvery grey banded leaves — one of the most beautiful of all bromeliads.

The growth and appearance of bromeliads are influenced greatly by their surroundings. Those varieties with smooth and brilliant leaves are natives of the rain forests, where favorable conditions are created by little variation in temperature and humidity. The rosettes are able to store water as a reserve for a less favorable time; therefore there is no need for scales on the leaves. In the rain forests there is always shade and little change in growing conditions. There you will find growing Vrieseas, Guzmanias, and some of the Tillandsias, such as *T. flabellata, T. grisebachiana, T. lindenii,* and others. All these plants need high temperature and humidity without periods of drying out. Protection from the sun is necessary for the successful growing of these plants, but dark, dank corners should be avoided.

In the next group of bromeliads, we find plants that will tolerate more light and lower temperatures. Among these are most of the Nidulariums and some of the Aechmeas, such as *Ae. fulgens* and *Ae. miniata* These plants should, accordingly, be kept less warm and given more light than those coming from the rain forests mentioned above.

Tillandsia streptophylla — One of the extreme epiphytes—no rosette—takes water exclusively through scales.

Closeup of a leaf of *T. streptophylla* showing the nearly cylindrical type of scale which enables the plant to absorb water and also helps to protect it from strong sunlight.

Next, we come to the bromeliads with visible scales. This group includes Neoregelias, Aechmeas, Billbergias, Cryptanthus, and a number of lesser known varieties. These bromeliads live under conditions where there are varying temperatures and where there are periods of no rainfall. As the rosettes cannot hold enough water for the periods of drought, these plants are provided by nature with numerous scales which help to catch any moisture, such as that which might be absorbed from nightly fogs. These bromeliads must also be given some protection from strong sunlight, although in the summer, they should be given as much light and air as possible. They do not mind a changing humidity and do not need to be kept too warm. Cryptanthus, however, are an exception, for they prefer a higher temperature and shade at all times. They will withstand a varying humidity. Aechmeas and Billbergias with heavy leaves and strong spines should not be grown too soft, for they are found in their native habitat growing under less favorable conditions.

Another group of bromeliads are the Tillandsias, which are the most epiphytic of all genera, and which are found growing under the most adverse conditions. Many Tillandsias form no rosette at all. The roots having no purpose other than to attach the plants to branches, Tillandsias of necessity must be endowed with extreme scales. As these plants are used to being surrounded by constantly moving air and plenty of light, they will not tolerate a constantly wet condition, but need to be dried out between waterings. Some need shade for growing and some will not tolerate direct sunlight. Tillandsias should not be kept too warm and should never be grown as houseplants, for the air would be too dry. They can, however, be grown in window boxes or in closed cases if the proper conditions can be provided.

Finally, there are the xerophytic bromeliads, such as Dykias and Hechtias, which are rarely grown in Europe. These plants are to be found growing with succulents, such as the Agave, in regions where there is little rainfall. As these bromeliads are terrestrials, they have a well-developed root system, which provides for the intake of water. Thus there is no need for scales, which are seldom found, if at all. These bromeliads should be grown cool, with but little water especially during the winter and lots of air and light at all times.

It is difficult to describe in detail the many varieties of bromeliads in a short article, but it is possible to find the right solution as to their cultural problems from a close observation of the plants.

Crimmitschau, D. D. R.

* * * *

QUESTION BOX

Q. Is *Vriesea splendens* propagated only by seed because it does not produce suckers? Can you tell me if there are any others like this and if so could you publish a list of them?

A. *V. splendens* can also be propagated by offshoots, but the manner of removing the offshoot is a bit more delicate and difficult than with most bromeliad species.

After the inflorescence of a plant has reached it maturity, the new shoot will appear near the axis next to the inflorescence instead of at, or near, the base of the plant as is usual with most bromeliads. When this new shoot has reached a height of five to six inches, it may be removed with a sharp knife. The operation is a delicate one as it is necessary to cut through the live tissue of the old plant which will separate nearly half of the plant. This cut must not injure the tissues of the new offshoots and the old basal leaves should be removed before cut is made.

If this operation is carefully done and the cut tissues treated with Captan, it is possible that the old plant may produce one to five successive offshoots from the uninjured side. These later plants may be, generally, more easily removed than the first one. It takes some courage as well as a surgeon's skill to attempt this operation, especially if you have only one plant in your possession.

Guzmania sanguinea will produce its new offshoot in the same location as *V. splendens.*

Many, if not most bromeliad plants, may be deliberately injured in the axis, so be careful to antiseptically treat it with Captan, so that rot or decay will not set in; offshoots, one or several, may then soon appear at the base of the plant—the main plant, of course, will not continue its growth. This procedure, of injuring the center, may be carried out even with seedlings, two or more inches in height.

Offshoots of *V. fenestralis,* generally, appear halfway between the axis and the basal leaves. These are more easily removed.   M. B. F.

POTTING MATERIAL FOR BROMELIADS

by Mulford B. Foster

What is the best potting material for bromeliads? This question is so often asked, not only by the amateur who has just discovered the charm of these decorative plants, but by the person who might have been growing them for some time.

The writer has been growing many kinds of bromelaids for the past twenty years and is just as anxious to experiment and to listen to other growers as he was the first year he began.

There is no one all inclusive answer to this very important question as any plant grower could quickly discover. When one realizes how many different conditions there are under which the bromeliads thrive and that a great number of them thrive in nature without any perceptible method of feeding, we marvel at their great ability to adapt themselves so well to the many ways and efforts of plant lovers and horticulturists to understand them.

Knowing that most of the bromeliads are acid loving plants will give us a basis on which to work. Some of them, however, which live on or near the sea coast must have some alkaline tolerance, but this may be taken care of by the leaves which must be tolerant to the salt air. This may account for the profuse flowering or lack of flowering of some species even more than the potting material.

Some of the bromeliads are so tolerant to many of us growers that we may continue to have them in our collections without finding out the really best method to prepare the potting material.

I feel, very definitely, that much more experimenting should be done by the growers and the results should be published in the Bulletin. This will be of equal importance to all, especially the bromeliads.

The most successful potting material formula which I have used for the majority of bromeliads has been a mixture of three shovels (or its equivalent) of sand, three shovels of leaf mold, and three shovels of a combination of German peat, shredded osmunda and/or sawdust; to this 3-3-3 mixture add ½ shovel of pulverized cow manure.

Leaf mold, I believe, is fundamental as a food for bromeliads since the majority of the species growing in trees, receive and retain falling leaves from the branches above. Which leaves are best I do not know. We use oak leaves. Do not use wild cherry leaves. When dried they will kill a goat and I have also found them very detrimental to most bromeliads, although many of our bromeliads are as tough as goats!

The sand in this mixture should be as coarse as possible; it can well include crushed granite for this is a very excellent acidifying agent for bromeliads. Many bromeliads grow natively on granite rocks and granitic soil in Brazil.

The German or Dutch peat, the shredded fresh osmunda fiber, or even fresh sawdust all serve to give acidity and aeration to the mixture.

Certan genera such as Vriesia, Guzmania, Tillandsia enjoy being potted in osmunda fiber only, just like an orchid, mainly because they usually need more aeration about their roots.

Remember this, however, that a certain mixture which does very well in Florida may not be the best in California or vice versa. Try the different methods, watch the results; change for newer experiments and then when you feel you have found something worthwhile, send it to your Bulletin.

Remember, always, bromeliads want good drainage . . . . lots of air . . . . moist atmosphere . . . . plenty of light. And quite naturally, they would prefer a bromeliad lover to take care of them.

When thinking about potting soil I always want, first of all, to consider in what soil the plant grows natively. This brings to mind that certain genera such as Thecophyllum, bromels closely related to Vriesias and Guzmanias, may be very selective as to the localities in which they thrive. Most of the Thecophyllum species are native to Costa Rica although they are found in other Central American and northern South American countries. So far as I know there have been few if any growers who have had any great degree of success in growing them. Many of the species are native to the volcanic mountains of those regions. Undoubtedly the volcanic ash in these areas gives off minerals and gasses which may, possibly, be especially benficial to these Theocophyllums.

Also another unknown factor of probable benefit to bromeliads is the air currents which carry air food to the bromeliads in their native haunts. The air factor is to be considered when we discover that it is not uncommon to find great quantities of bromels growing in the trees on one side of a mountain and very few just across the opposite side of the valley.

In considering these factors which we cannot give the bromeliads so readily when we transfer them to our greenhouses, it would seem that we must find a substitute for them, and in addition to our regular potting formulas I believe we should also use liquid fertilizers which will supply additional nutrients and give us greater success with bromeliads.

In the small amount of experimenting by trial and error methods the results have not been near as efficient as the adaptability of the bromels themselves in learning to live with us in spite of conditions.

This amazing adaptability has been developed through long centuries of the rise and fall of the great land masses which harbored bromeliads. The first members of the bromeliad family were terrestial plants depending on their roots for food but the great changes of conditions in those areas have caused the more recent species to adapt themselves to an epiphytic (1) or saxicolus (2) way of life. The roots had to become more hold-fast implements than feeding organs and the leaves have gradually functioned as feeder parts.

When we bring these plants into our homes and greenhouses we have eliminated the possibility of the plants catching leaves and decaying material that would be falling from the forest trees into their cups to be used by them as food, as they must adapt themselves to the new conditions and revert to their ancestral habit of feeding through their roots as do most of the other plants on the earth.

In making any horticultural suggestions for the better growing of bromeliads, I make them, always with reservations. Because there can usually be found exceptions to any broad cultural statement. And in transplanting bromeliads

84

from South America some very baffling situations appear and it is very thought provoking as to what to do to solve the situation. I might relate just one of many such situations which I have encountered and still do not know the answer.

In Columbia, South America, I found both *Guzmania lingulata* and *Guzmania musaica,* two beautiful species, growing side by side on the same tree trunk, both very vigorous. I brought a few plants of each species home with me. But, here in my Florida greenhouse, with both species receiving the same treatment, the result is quite different. *G. lingulata* thrives and blooms, but *G. musaica* finally pines away.

This is only one of the many experiences that have happened and it is all the more baffling because of the fact that both plants thrived so beautifully together in their native habitat.

Thus, in growing bromeliads, acid food as nearly resembling nature's own compost as possible, and favorable air currents are two factors having considerable influence in success with these plants living under our conditions rather than theirs. The other two factors of light and temperature will be under discussion in another issue.

It will be a great help and service to both yourself and to the plants and to all who are striving to understand their needs, if you will record your experiences and let other Society members know about it through the Bulletin.

INDUCTION OF FLOWERING OF BROMELIADS

Roger K. Taylor

The exposure of bromeliads to an atmosphere containing a low concentration of ethylene or acetylene gas is known, in many cases, to initiate the formation of bloom spikes. One suggested procedure is to dissolve a little calcium carbide in water and pour the resulting acetylene solution into the leaf cups; another, to add carbide directly to the water in the cups, generating the acetylene *in situ.* A disadvantage of both of these schemes is the distinct possibility of damage to the plant by the alkaline residue from the carbide.

An alternate method, avoiding this risk, is to place the plants for treatment in a Wardian case or other enclosure along with a lump of carbide; water vapor slowly reacts with the carbide to release acetylene. A twenty-four hour exposure has proven effective with some Aechmeas and most of the Billbergias tried. If the plants fail to respond, a repetition with perhaps a larger quantity of carbide or a longer time may be tried.

Anyone having access to either ethylene or acetylene in compressed-gas cylinders might prepare a solution by bubbling a slow flow of the gas into water, and pour the solution into the plant; this procedure should be as innocuous as the preceding.

A word of caution may be in order: acetylene with air forms a particularly wide range of explosive mixtures, so, though the concentrations should be safely low, it would be as well to keep open flames away.

BROMELIADS CAN TAKE IT

Victoria Padilla

Except for the ruins of a temple in the background, the above picture might well have been photographed on the moon—so barren is the aspect. Indeed the scene appears so forbidding that it is hard to believe that any vegetation at all could survive, and none does with the exception of the stalwart bromeliad.

The country in this photo is Peru, the bromeliad probably *Tillandsia platyphylla,* the species common to the area bordering the Pacific Ocean. Bromeliads are about the only plants to be found on the desolate coastal deserts of Peru. As they are plants of the air, they are not dependent upon the earth for their sustenance, so can survive where other plants cannot.

If bromeliads do not look to the earth for their nourishment, is it necessary for us to worry very much about the compost in which we pot them? At a recent meeting of the Southern California Bromeliad Society it was the consensus that the potting medium is not important as long as the plant has good drainage, the proper amount of light, and plenty of humidity. A survey taken of the various kinds of potting media used would indicate that this is indeed true. Here are some of the potting materials used by various members of the Society—there are doubtless many more.

1. osmunda fiber
2. fir bark
3. a mixture of fir bark, peat, sponge rock
4. shredded hapu (Hawaiian fernwood)
5. fir bark, sticks, and leaves

6. redwood shavings
7. leaf mold
8. 1/3 humus, 1/3 builder's sand, 1/3 peat
9. dried kelp, pumice stone, tan bark, and several nutrients
10. commercial cymbidium mix (a mixture of sand, fir bark peat, shaved hoof and horn)
11. fir bark and manure - 10 to 1
12. commercial cattleya mix (fir bark, shavings, dolmite line, shaved hoof and horn

The question then arises - is fertilizing necessary? With the exception of materials such as leaves, earth particles, bird excrement, insects, and the like that fall into their cups, bromeliads in their native state receive little nourishment. Most members of the Society agree, however, that plants grown under artificial conditions in the home or greenhouse need a little extra encouragement in the way of an occasional feeding, although there are a few who believe that fertilizing is unnecessary and have beautiful plants to back this opinion. Procedures vary among those growers who fertilize. Some feed their plants every two weeks, some once a month, some once a season. Some fertilize during the summer only, some the year round. The kinds of fertilizer used also differ considerably, although most members prefer foliar feeding. In those areas where there is little rainfall and the water tends to be alkaline, it has been found that frequent feeding with weak solutions of an acid fertilizer is beneficial.

Too often we tend to pamper our bromeliads, forgetting that in their natural habitat, they have to withstand all kinds of adverse conditions. Many times I have entered the greenhouses of friends to be told to close the door immediately so that no draft would blow in on the plants. No greenhouse subject enjoys a sudden blast of cold air, but bromeliads are *air* plants and need all the air they can get. Mr. Goodale Moir of Honolulu, who has gathered orchids and bromeliads in the American jungles, recently told me that he seldom, if ever, found any epiphytes where there was not a good current of air at all times. A friend who has just returned from a botanic exposition to the head waters of the Amazon commented on the fact that the most exciting floral display that she saw was in a narrow valley situated between the towns of Loja and Zamora in southern Ecuador. Here the wind blew relentlessly night and day; in fact the valley was a veritable wind tunnel, the whirlblast being so strong that it was difficult for a person to stand up against it. But the orchids and bromeliads presented an unforgettable sight—for beauty of flower and magnificence and size of plant surpassing anything that she saw on her entire trip. She counted twelve genera of bromeliads all in perfect bloom and many others which for beauty of foliage did not need to be in flower to be striking plants.

Although none of us would think of turning our greenhouses into wind tunnels, we should see to it that the air in our houses is at all times fresh. A revolving fan judiciously placed on one corner of a wall can well take the place of the gentle breezes that our air plants like so well.

GROWING BROMELIADS IN OPEN GROUND

Joseph Schneider

While the majority of the most beautiful and ornamental species of bromeliads coming from the tropical forests of South America are strictly epiphytic and can be brought to show their full beauty only under glass with temperature and humidity under control, there are many worthwhile attractive species quite amenable for growing in the open ground (some preferably so) with a minimum of shelter in places where temperatures do not fall too low and some protection from the hot burning sun and dehydrating desert winds can be provided. Plant lovers without glasshouse facilities need not forgo the pleasure of their successful cultivation and can enjoy their fascinating beauty without too great difficulties.

The easiest and most adaptable bromels are of the xerophytic type, the group whose members resemble small agaves and aloes in appearance, and like them can take tough conditions, necessary neglect and adverse weather without much harm.

Most Dyckias will thrive well even in poor dry ground or rocky soil. Like our native Agaves, Dudleyas, and Echeverias, they will withstand hot sun, long dry spells, moderate frosts if the ground is not too loose and sandy or too shallow. *Dyckia brevifolia* (*sulphurea*) makes large tight mounds. *Dyckia altissima*, both varieties, does equally well. *Dyckia rariflora* and its varieties, *remotiflora*, etc., will not develop as long leaves as under glass but will grow more compact and flower and multiply even better in the open soil. They form large clumps, their stolons coming up near the mother plant. Dyckias form seed readily and plentifully and self-sow, but the tiny seedlings succumb to the first dry spell. I believe they would readily naturalize if browsing animals could be guarded against.

Ananas comosus (*sativus*) will grow from a rooted top and bear a pineapple in three years—it should have some shade. *Ananas ananasoides* grows even easier and forms more offsets. The small, often vividly banded and colored ornamental dwarf pineapples are too rare and precious to be risked in an outdoor planting.

Hechtias, with their loose rosettes of gracefully recurved leaves, grow slowly enough to be manageable and do well. *Hechtia texensis* is probably the only one available and seems to be somewhat more tender than Dyckias, suffering below twenty degrees.

Puya spathacea is rather large, about three feet wide and as high at flowering size. It has a red stemmed branched inflorescence; the flowers being small, dark blue-green. It is very showy, easy to grow, and will flower five to six years from seed.

Puya alpestris in flower is an incomparable sight. Most will agree that this is surely one of the most beautiful flowering plants of the world. A magnificent yucca-like spike, with fifty, one hundred, and more individual flowers, the gleaming orange stamens emerging from the depth of nectar filled chalices of somber blue-green of a metalic sheen awakes in one a feeling of mystic wonder. To my knowledge these two Puyas are the only ones available at present from nurseries.

Bromelia serra and *Bromelia balansae* are, like Puyas, armed with little hooked spines, but to see their "Hearts of fire" in their glorious beauty should warrant them a place in spite of the spines. They are very easily satisfied with almost any place allotted to them, growing without care.

Other xerophytic and semi-xerophytic species available and suitable are Ochagavia, *Aechmea recurvata* (ortgiesii) Fascicularias, etc. Many Billbergias and their hybrids, and the larger leaved Aechmeas and their hybrids, will readily take to open ground. So will some Neoregelias, Quesnelias, etc. Many do even better in open soil and when left undisturbed, form large clumps. Five to ten year old specimens may have from twenty to fifty flower spikes at one time and show in this way a beauty that no small glasshouse plant can equal. Some of the vigorous Billbergia and Aechmea hybrids mature their offshoots quickly and flower in succession so that an old plant often is in bloom throughout most of the year.

The above plants take most readily to the root-debris around palms. There they can anchor their roots, find enough nourishment and sustaining moisture to grow to an astonishing size. They may burn a little in summer and will not have the dark succulence of glass protected plants, but they flower and multiply. In planting avoid the "drip-zone" that is the outer edge of the umbrella of the Phoenix. Give Nidulariums and the soft leaved Aechmeas the most shaded side.

Outdoor growing does bring a few problems the glasshouse growers are spared. The foremost is pest-control. If the ground is infested with ground mealy-bugs or root-aphis, they must be cleaned up first. Scale will build up in summer and should be held down with a nicotine sulfate or a little oil. One of the most troublesome pests is snails and also slugs that find the dark moist leaf-cups an ideal hiding place. They should be washed out with a hose.

If your water is at all alkaline or hard, do not attempt to keep the leaf cups filled with water. If cold should damage plants, cut off this frozen part as soon as possible before rot sets in and wanders into the basal part. The woody caudex has generally enough dormant buds to give the plant a fresh start.

Fortunately, most of the above mentioned bromels are almost unbelievably adaptable, clinging to life with a tenacity so that nothing but total dehydration or freezing seems to be too much for them. They may not be at their splendid best if they have to rough it in open ground, but they will do well enough to delight you with their unusual beauty and strange form and make a bromeliad enthusiast of you, leading to increasing enjoyment as you become more familiar with this group of plants.

And please note—any cultural hints apply only to conditions prevalent in the vicinity of Los Angeles and should be modified according to conditions existing in other areas.

San Gabriel, California.

HAWAIIAN TREE FERN FIBER AS A POTTING MEDIUM

DAVID BARRY, JR.

T HE ROOTS OF THE HAWAIIAN FERNS of the genus Cibotium grow down the outside of the trunks from the base of the leaves to the ground. In time and as ferns grow in height a dense mat of fern fiber is formed around the trunk. In Hawaii this mat is called hapuu. It is harvested in great quantities by cutting down the ferns. The terminal crown is generally left on the ground and often begins to form a new trunk as the exterior roots descend. It does not make much difference whether or not the severed terminal is left on its side, or upright, as long as it is in a moist spot.

The mat of fiber is offered in various shapes, such as hunks, slabs, rafts, the hollowed-out sides of pots, and as shredded material. It is very heavy with moisture unless dried. Sometimes this drying is done in a kiln. On the other hand, the material as fiber is sometimes sold in a damp condition and kept in moisture-retaining bags. As such it has been dubbed "live hapuu," the inference being that hapuu that has retained the natural moisture from rainfall is superior to hapuu that has had its moisture restored by hand of man. This contention is conjectural at this time.

The use of fern fiber as a potting medium for epiphytes is time-honored cultural practice. Root fiber from the osmunda fern has been the classic medium for many years in potting orchids. There is presently a large traffic in the fiber of Mexican tree ferns. What is new is that the practice of using Hawaiian hapuu for potting bromeliads and orchids began on a large scale in Southern California about two years ago, and has produced important and beneficial results, particularly with bromeliads. Here are some of the advantages of hapuu over other potting media:

1. The water supply of Southern California is slightly alkaline. The rain that falls on epiphytes is never alkaline and when diluted with the decomposition of organic matter found on the branches of trees around the roots of plants becomes slightly acid. It has been evident that epiphytes do not like the local water. The longer plants are kept in the same pot and with the same medium (before hapuu) the greater was the accumulation of alkalinity in the pot and the more the plants suffered. One of several ways in which they showed their unhappiness was by brown-tipping of the leaves. Some plants resented the alkalinity to such an extent that they would hardly stay alive and became wretched specimens. This was notably so with *Aechmea tessmannii*. After repotting these plants in hapuu the change from narrow, shrivelled, brown-tipped leaves to wide, larger and perfectly formed leaves took place quickly. Why? Water did not linger in the pot. It ran right on through and got little chance to build up an alkaline content. The fern fiber was moistened around the roots as would a passing rain moisten the root of a plant on the bough of a tree. The change was spectacular.

2. Hapuu lasts for many years and will not break down into a paste as osmunda will in time.

3. Hapuu affords a very high degree of aeration which is a condition that epiphytes enjoy naturally and that is difficult to provide with denser media.

4. Hapuu is wiry and springy. When plants are potted firmly with it they are held tightly in the pot. Epiphytes grow firmly attached to the host that supports them. They hold on with great tenacity and sometimes it takes much strength to pull them off. It is evident that bromeliads should never be permitted to be loose in the pot.

In using hapuu it is necessary to feed more often as much of the fertilizer runs out with the water before it can be utilized. It is probably necessary to feed twice as much as with denser media.

The use of hapuu has revolutionized the growing of bromeliads in Southern California within the last two years, and has made it a much more rewarding effort.

— *11977 San Vicente Blvd., Los Angeles 49, California.*

*   *   *   *

WATER AND NUTRIENT UPTAKE OF BROMELIADS
PETER TEMPLE

(From studies carried out by Mr. J. Sieber, biologist in the Botanical Institution in Munich, West Germany.)

Water and nutrient uptake was studied in *Aechmea fasciata, Nidularium innocentii, Guzmania tricolor,* and *Vriesea splendens* at all stages from germination to mature, flowering plants. Absorption through roots or leaves was equally effective and occured in plants from the youngest stages onwards. In an absorptive humus substrate, root nutrition produced better growth than leaf nutrition; in a less absorptive medium leaf nutrition gave better results. Combined leaf and root nutrition was particularly effective, except in young plants. At the youngest stages, root nutrition was more important than leaf nutrition, but the position was reversed with increasing age. Root growth was stimulated more by root nutrition than by leaf nutrition. Growth of unpotted plants receiving leaf nutrients was increased by high relative humidities.

Plants of *Aechmea fasciata* fed through the leaves developed loose, pendulous growth with long leaves and a relatively long inflorescence. With root nutrition, growth was more compact, with broader, upright leaves of a clear green, the inflorescence was relatively short. In *Nidularium innocentii* nitrogen was most readily absorbed through the leaves and P O and K O through the roots. Nutrient solutions were absorbed more quickly than water by *Aechmea fasciata.* — *42 Holly Park, Finchley, London, England.*

LIGHT AND SHADE

One very important factor in the growing of bromeliads is that of light. Bromeliads like plenty of light, and by far the majority of them develop their best character, color and form when this factor is properly provided.

As there are three subfamilies in the bromeliads, so there are three types of light conditions for these different divisions. Most of the Pitcairnioideae, such as members of the genera Dyckia, Puya, Encholirium, and Hechtia require full sun for their best form. The drooping grass-like Pitcairnias may ask for a bit more shade. Practically all of the members of the genus Bromelia are best in the sun or partial shade. However, most of them will grow in shade but they will be more rank in growth and more difficult to handle. In fact, there are comparatively few bromeliads that will not thrive in shade or semi-shade. But the xerophytic types of Tillandsias, broad-leafed types of Vriesia-like Tillandsias and almost any of the stiff-leafed members of the Bromelioideae such as Aechmea, Hohenbergia and similar types will definitely have finer color and form with an abundance of light and air.

In almost all plants the texture of the leaf is one of the first signs that will tell you whether the plant can withstand much light or not. Most of the Vriesias, Guzmanias, Billbergias, Neoregelias like plenty of light for their best development yet very few of them want full sunlight outside and almost none of them want full sunlight if they are under glass, especially in the summer time. In the north, many greenhouses use very sparse shading during the winter because the sun is at such an angle that the rays do not burn through the glass. This same treatment could not be given in the tropics or subtropics where the sun is much hotter and more direct even in the winter.

Slats over the glass will break up the light for many of the bromels much better than an opaque shading compound. It gives more of the effect of the filtered light coming down here and there as through the forest trees.

Light problems may be ever present and they change with the seasons. It may often be wise to change the positions of your plants from summer to winter. A plant, for example, like *Aechmea schultesiana* will have a beautiful deep maroon red coloring if it has an abundance of light in the winter time, but the same plant may turn green with almost no trace of the red showing if it is in too much shade in the summer. Also, the leaves will be longer, and less stiff until the plant will become almost unrecognizable so far as the shape and color are concerned. Some bromeliads may be quite healthy and have vigorous growth but because of insufficient light, may loose their naturally beautiful shape and color.

Xerophytic plants may be hung successfully near the glass and produce their fullest character. The same light would burn or dry up a shade-requiring Vriesia or Guzmania.

It is best to study the different positions in your home or greenhouse at different times of the year and treat your plants accordingly. They will appreciate your consideration.

GROWING BROMELIADS AS HOUSE PLANTS

DR. GEORGE MILSTEIN

W E MEMBERS, who live in the New York area have a plant-growing problem which is peculiar to us. Most of us, with few exceptions, live in apartment houses with poor lighting conditions and an excessive dryness in the winter due to the steam heat with which our homes are warmed. Most of us, also, cannot grow our plants out of doors in the summer, which makes it extremely difficult to establish sturdy leaves and flower buds. In spite of these seemingly unsurmountable obstacles, many of us do grow a great variety of bromeliads, including many of the so-called difficult ones, and we not only have healthy plants but we bloom them, also.

Three things are primarily necessary in order to grow bromeliads: proper light, proper moisture, and space to grow the plants. The following is what I found to be successful in my circumstances; I pass them along for what they are worth.

Since I must assume that this article will be read by genuine enthusiasts, I must also assume that more than just a few bromeliads will be grown. One of my specialties is Tillandsias. In order to grow more than 100 different plants, I have worked out a method to utilize every bit of window space. I am fortunate in having a large picture window in my living room with a southern exposure. Instead of drapes or curtains, we hang a bamboo trellis from long projecting arms in the window. (see Fig. 1.) All the Tillandsias are fastened to pieces of hapuu tree-fern. Each slab of hapuu is attached to a length of soft, heavy iron wire which is bent to form a hook to suspend the plant from the bamboo crosspieces. The window ledge is reserved for potted bromeliads which are coming into flower and need the direct sunshine for "coloring-up" (this will be explained later in the article). This "bamboo curtain" can be quite attractive. If the bamboo trellis is made of two individual sections, each of which is suspended from a swinging drape holder on each side of the window, the trellis can be easily moved for access to the window.

Another method of growing bromeliads is on driftwood or tree-fern arrangements. I have found cholla sections to be very effective. In Vol. XIII, No. 4, page 83 of the *Bromeliad Bulletin,* there is a photo showing a tree I made of cholla pieces glued and wired together. This tree supports more than 30 large bromels and is set in concrete in a brass container on casters, so it can be moved about. The cholla is stuffed with a mixture of sphagnum and German peat moss. Eventually, the roots of the bromeliads will grow through the interstices of the cholla and will be able to take hold in the stuffing. The mosses can hold a lot of moisture without getting too soggy. One of the simplest methods of growing a great quantity of bromeliads is on tables under lights (see Fig. 2). This is not too attractive, but it is undoubtedly the easiest and the least expensive of all the methods I use.

Next to the space problem, the next most difficult item in growing bromeliads is maintaining a proper moisture and humidity balance in the growing area. The first thing I did was cut off the heat in the living room. This room is properly and sufficiently taken care of by the heat which seeps in from the other rooms. The easiest and best way to establish and maintain a proper humidity for bromeliads is through the use of an electric humidifier which will vaporize a few gallons of water into the atmosphere every day. Another method is shown in Fig. 3. Make a simple frame of scrap lumber large

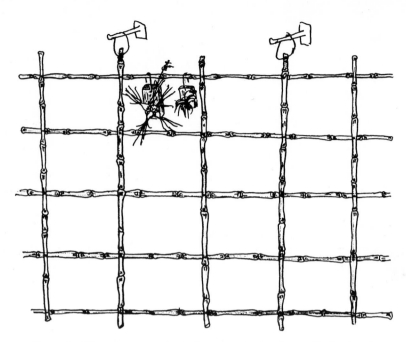

Figure 1—Illustrates one method of constructing bamboo trellis for hanging epiphytes. Two are shown on hapuu slabs suspended from the upper bar of the trellis by means of soft malleable black iron wire.

enough to cover the area decided upon. To this, tack a sheet of plastic loose enough to rest on the bottom. Fill the cavity with pumice rock chunks and thoroughly soak them with water. The potted plants can be placed on this support and a certain amount of dampness will permeate the air. Another method is to use a hand vaporizer a few times a day. This is practical when only a few plants are grown. To the water which is used in the electric humidifier or the hand vaporizer, a complete plant food can be added. This will help to feed the plants. Every Sunday, I fill the bathtub with water. I then unhook all my Tillandsias from the bamboo and dunk them for a sufficient time to permit the hapuu to soak up the optimum capacity of water. Since the average bathtub will only hold about 20 to 25 plants at a time, I have to do the soaking in relays. It is a good idea to get a plastic washtub to carry the wet plants in, back to the bamboo, otherwise a sloppy wet floor will cause a domestic crisis. Of course, normal watering into the tanks of the bromeliads and into the flowerpots will be a matter of routine.

Proper lighting of bromeliads can be rather tricky, and is open to a lot of controversy. In order to grow a great number of bromeliads indoors, it is necessary for us to rely to a greater or lesser extent on some form of artificial light. Since incandescent light gives

Collecting Bromeliads along the Amazon

Aechmea chantinii
A native of the
Amazon region in
Peru

Bromeliads as a part of the landscape design.

Above—*Portea petropolitana* var. *extensa* in a rock garden

Lower right—Neoregelias by the side of a pool

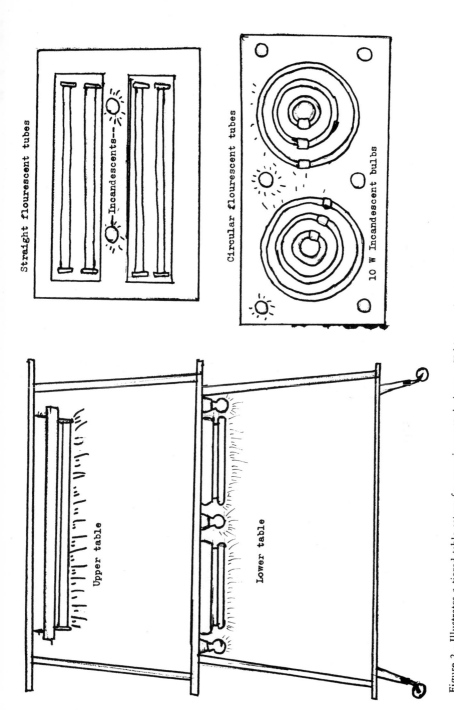

Figure 2—Illustrates a tiered table set-up for growing potted plants. Tables are about 5 x 3 feet and the tops are made of 3/4-exterior plywood. The straight tubes on the upper table give off 160 watts of light. The lower table, using circular tubes, gives off 192 watts of light.

Straight flourescent tubes

Incandescents

Circular flourescent tubes

10 W Incandescent bulbs

Upper table

Lower table

off an immense amount of heat, fluorescent tubes or circles are almost always chosen. There has been much material, both pro and con, written about the new plant growing bulbs such as "Gro-lux". I can only give you my own experiences using these lights. I must confess that as far as bromeliads are concerned, these lights are of no especial advantage. With every 100 watts of fluorescent light, mix in 10 to 15% incandescent light. On seedlings and very young plants, the lights should be no more than 8 or 10 inches away. In the case of larger plants, the lights can be 12 to 15 inches away. The lights are connected through an automatic timer which turns the lights on and off without any attention. These are set to give a least 12 to 14 hours of light a day. Naturally with so much steady light, more water and more plant food than usual is necessary. I prefer the multiple circular fluorescent fixtures, as these concentrate a tremendous amount of in a given space. Now comes the great flaw in fluorescent lighting, at least, as far as I have discovered in the case of bromeliads. In my experience, the plants will grow and even bloom under artificial lights but they do not color up too well. In the early part of this article, I mentioned reserving the window ledge for "coloring up" space. When it is time for the plants to color, I move them to the sunny window. Somehow it takes natural sunlight to redden the leaves of *Neoregelias, Cryptanthus bromelioides tricolor, Vriesea splendens* spikes, *Guzmania lingulata* inflorescense, and many of the *Aechmeas*.

One more thing is necessary to insure healthy growth of bromeliads, and that is proper ventilation. Of course, in the summer time, this is no problem. In the winter, however, this can be rather risky in the New York area. I have solved this problem in my case by opening the windows in another room and by the use of electric fans circulating

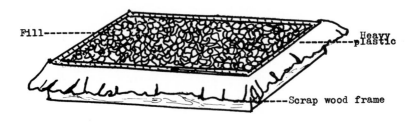

Figure 3—Sketch shows frame constructed of 4 pieces of scrap 1" lumber, at least 2 inches wide and long enough to fill the desired space. A sheet of heavy gauge waterproof plastic is loosely placed inside of the frame to form the bottom and is fastened by tacks to the upper edge of the frame. The excess plastic is allowed to extend over the sides of the frame and if tucked under will effectively cover the bare wood. Large pebbles, pumice rock, gravel or vermiculite is used to fill in the frame and when this material is soaked in water, it will give off moisture over a long period.

fresh air into the room where the plants are growing. Naturally, on the days when the weather is too treacherous, this procedure is omitted.

All the above methods assume that one starts with healthy young plants. While it is possible to nurse sickly plants back to good health in a greenhouse or out of doors, it is a difficult thing to do in house horticulture. Besides, space is too precious to waste indoors. As one can gather, it takes a lot of effort to grow bromeliads indoors, but I am assuming that this is being read by the same sort of "Bromel-nut" that I am. We are prepared, even anxious to exert time and energy to cultivate our favorite plants. With care, all of the so-called difficult types can be grown successfully in the home, including the Tillandsias, Guzmanias, Vrieseas, Nidulariums, etc. The most important ingredients include love for bromeliads, a willingness to work, and a great amount of patience. I almost forgot to mention the most important ingredient—a loving and understanding mate.

8502 Fort Hamilton Parkway, Brooklyn, N. Y. 11209

* * *

MOISTURE INDICATOR

W. B. CHARLEY

WHAT UNCOMPLIMENTARY THOUGHTS WE HARBOR and even give voice to upon discovering invaders growing in the top soil of bromeliad pots in our glasshouses! Where these come from is often a puzzle. Among such invaders one finds weeds and also harmless ferns, lichens, etc. If we are drastic in pulling out the weeds, we could be sympathetic with the harmless things and even give consideration to them.

No matter how carefully we water a greenhouse, there are always those pots, sheltered by overhanging leaves from another plant, or those on high shelves which miss out on their drink. These bromeliads may not show any set back for a long time, but are slowly dying from the roots, and a bromel doing this does not usually survive, especially young plants.

This is where the invaders, mentioned above, come in. If we draft the good from the bad, and the little plants are allowed to grow and overhang the pots, we can be sure that the plant is getting its needed watering if we see these happily growing and indicating that water in the pot mix is present. If there are no mosses, etc., these could be put in deliberately, and they could even enhance the look of a lovely bromeliad, though care should be used to see that no seeding types are used.

It has been the writer's experience to find a large bromeliad in a large pot with the pot mix bone dry. This was amazing and could not be accounted for, as the glasshouse was carefully (?) watered every day.

If a small foreign plant had been there and was flourishing, this could not have happened. — *The Jungle Bromeliadium, Mt. Tomah, Bilpin, N. S. W., Australia.*

BROMELIADS ON DISPLAY

E. H. PALMER

Sid Avery & Associates

Decorations for a luncheon of the Men's
Garden Club of Los Angeles

THERE IS NOTHING MORE ANNOYING than to have a fine plant, perfect in every respect and eminently "show-worthy," and to find one morning that a pest or pests have caused a disfigurement of one or more of the leaves.

Perhaps in Florida we have more pests than in other locations. I do not think so, but pests thrive the year round! Chief of these is the red spider that ruined the pineapple crop many years ago. Although it is not so much of a problem today, there are occasions when it is evident. A very close inspection with powerful magnifying lenses will sometimes disclose such evidence, especially in young seedlings. But there are other pests that work inimically to perfect plant growth.

Right here, I know I am going to mention things that are usually decried, but, nonetheless, do exist. Scale is not the only despoiler of bromeliads! It is a lovely day, the door of the greenhouse or shade house is left open, a "miller" pops in, lays a few eggs on tender leaves, especially on young seedlings; and overnight, it seems, a dirty little worm has eaten his fill. Or, perhaps, a cricket has chosen to sit on a leaf in the night and has chewed a ragged hole, or, again, a small snail may embed himself between two leaves. Also mealy-bugs or cottony scale may find their way deep down between two leaves. Even in the open garden wild rabbits and young deer seem to like the taste or flavor of those prickly Dyckia leaves.

All of this indicates that no matter how carefully bromeliads are grown, or in

98

what latitude, or under what conditions, there are insect pests that discover something they like in bromeliads and can overnight ruin the show-worthiness of a plant. There is only one answer to this problem: constant vigilance and frequent treatment with pesticides.

It has been said that bromeliads are free from the pests that are usually a problem when growing other plants, and to a great extent this is true. However, the foregoing points out the necessity for proper care. This, in the case of bromeliads, is quite simple; hence the oft-repeated comment that bromeliads are easy to take care of.

There are four varieties of scale that appear to favor bromeliads. Unfortunately, once the scale situation has been discovered, it is usually too late to do anything; for even after removal, the scale leaves a whitish area that is a disfiguration of the plant. Some scale also moves slightly and leave a brownish line of a quarter inch or so. A beautiful *Neoregelia marmorata* was brought to show recently. It had been infested with scale and although the plant had been cleaned up and no live scale was apparent, the plant was nevertheless completely disqualified for any honor.

One of the best remedies for such scale is the use of a Malathion dip. Malathion in an oil emulsion should never be used, as any oil base is injurious to bromeliads in that it affects the "air" or "breathing" conditions so vital to these plants. The dry powder, readily obtainable, is mixed with water at the rate of two teaspoonsful to a gallon of water. An old garbage can or lard pail can be used for this purpose. When the solution is thoroughly mixed—stirred constantly for at least one minute— a cloth should be placed around the base of the plant to hold the soil or potting medium, then the water within the cup emptied, and the plant immersed in the solution, upside down. Care must be taken to see that the solution gets into all the crevises. After the plant is lifted out of the solution, care should be taken to see that there is none left in the plant, and the plant laid sideways or in a position from which any surplus liquid will drain out. This procedure leaves a film of the solution on the leaves of the plant. After 15 to 30 minutes have elapsed, the plant should be rinsed with clear water, the cup refilled with water, preferably with a trace of nutriment therein.

The solution should not be made any stronger and should not be allowed to stand in the cups for more than a few minutes. The cups should not be scrubbed. The drying-out process should not last for more than one hour at the most and then the plant should be rinsed thoroughly and filled with fresh, clean water—rain water being preferable.

Should this process still permit a few scale insects to remain, it should be repeated in a day or so. Normally, however, this process, repeated every two to four weeks, should keep your plants clear of scale and even of other insects that may cause damage to your plants. In the case of a rare (and it is quite rare) infestation of mealy-bugs or cottony scale, it will be necessary, in addition to the foregoing process, to take a small camel's hair brush, dip it in the solution and brush out the infestation. Those tiny snails may also be reached with such a brush which will not injure a leaf in any way. Red spider sometimes attacks young seedlings, and they may be treated with the Malathion solution, but at about half the foregoing strength.

Some commercial growers use other formulae and have also tried certain trade-name insecticides, but for the hobbyist, the grower of a few bromeliads, the above process is well worth abiding by.   Again, don't use any oil sprays or oil of any kind on bromeliads.   Do not try Parathion, which is stronger than Malathion and very effective, but very dangerous for an inexperienced person to use.   And do not use slug bait around your plants, one falling in a cup would kill that plant.   And as a final word of caution—do use rubber gloves when dipping!

Generally speaking, a weekly or bi-weekly careful inspection of your plants and then a dipping in the solution will save a great deal of time that might be consumed if the plants were allowed to go until infestation was perfectly obvious.   It is also a time saver to see that the water in the cups does not become spoiled or contaminated. Mosquitoes and other insects are far less likely to make a home of the cups if water is kept fresh and sweet.   Of course, one cannot follow this procedure "way down South" when the plants are in the open in a garden or on a "bromeliad tree," but frequently wash out the cups.

Here, then is a simple and easy way to protect your plants from depredations by various insect pests.   It is all a part of the fun and joy in growing show-worthy bromeliads.   —10301 — 65th Avenue, Largo, Florida

Guzmania lingulata var. *lingulata*

100

WATERING

There is much pro and con regarding the watering of bromeliads, but there seems to be little disagreement that bromeliads do need water. The natural confirmation of these plants with their leaves so formed to hold water is proof of this.

In trying to establish a criterion for watering in cultivation it is best to find out first what nature has done. There are three distinct types of bromeliads which in nature have equally distinct watering requirements. When we bring these different ones into cultivation we need to blend the conditions, being at the same time fully aware of their diverse needs.

There are many types of forests and arid areas where bromels live; these conditions naturally present different watering problems.

1. The xerophytic types with densely tomentose leaves in twisted rosettes like most Tillandsias which live in or near the treetops and in more open places on rocky side of mountains or ledges, are exposed to wind and a dry atmosphere and a lack of rain. However, these plants in most instances receive more water than is evident because they have a "drink" every night from heavy dew in higher altitudes, or from wind carried moisture if near the sea. Although these plants may go for weeks without receiving direct rain, generally speaking, they would not thrive in your greenhouse or home unless they received frequent waterings.

2. The dense forest types which live in more shade and generally nearer the ground tend, characteristically, to have thinner and smoother leaves. These rosette shaped plants have water reservoirs at the base of each leaf and are accustomed to a more constant humid condition with less fluctuation and less air movement. In cultivation they accordingly must have more moisture to keep them in good growing condition than the more xerophytic types. These plants will be principally Vriesias, Guzmanias and the more glossy leaf types of Aechmeas such as *Ae. Weilbachii, Ae. miniata, Ae. Racinae,* etc. This same condition will apply to the *Neoregelia carolinae* type of plant and practically all of the Nidulariums as they, too, are moisture loving plants which for the most part grow near or on the ground in a rain forest.

3. The xerophytic type of terrestrial bromels such as Dyckia, Hechtia, Bromelia, Puya, Deuterocohnia have a great resistance to drouth, at the same time can stand rather heavy rainy conditions provided they are established with good drainage. These plants do not require so much watering as the shady forest types because many of them have thicker and more succulent leaves as a result of the greater light exposure.

It would be quite possible to give virtually the same amount of water to all these different types of bromeliads in your greenhouse if they were placed in positions there according to their individual requirements. If Tillandsias and the more xerophytic types with harsher and tougher leaves were placed in higher or more airy and lighter positions they would dry out much sooner and therefore not be subjected to as much moisture as the ones placed in a lower or shadier position.

When bringing the bromels into cultivation we must first consider the temperature factor. In a home or a greenhouse when temperature is high the evaporation in the plant cups and in the potting medium around the roots is greater, therefore give more water to the bromels. Temperatures above 75° F. means more drying, so they will need to be syringed daily or even twice daily in extremely hot weather even though their cups might be full of water. This extra watering can be done only if the soil be very porous and allows the water to seep through quickly.

The humidity in your house or greenhouse with its proper movement of air is the biggest factor to govern the amount and frequency of watering.

If the plants are in your home and they lack the open air at all times, they would enjoy whenever possible, a shower in the rain outside. Rain water has a pH factor of more or less 6.8 or slightly on the acid side so it is best if the water you use does not test above 8.0 on the Hydrion Charts.

Water is the most important factor in the life of any plant and especially the bromeliads. Water containing excessive amounts of lime or salt is detrimental to many species, and it may be beneficial to empty the water in the cups at times or to add rain water or weak solutions of acid water to counteract the alkaline condition. I believe it is a known fact that the city water on one side of Los Angeles is different from that of the other side . . . and that the bromeliads thrive accordingly. If the water is alkaline, then it would be a wise thing for the grower to use rain water or make it possible for his bromeliads to enjoy a shower of rain every now and then.

If you are growing these plants on an extensive scale and your water is alkaline, then one of the known available systems of treating water should be used.

What happens to the water after it has stood in a bromel for a few days without renewal? Generally speaking, the water in the center of the young plants which have not yet bloomed is clear. The outer or lower leaves of these immature plants hold the most water where often is found material such as leaves and small twigs which, when finally decayed, furnish food for absorption into the heart of the plant. However, not all the water contained in the bromeliad leaf cups is pure and undefiled. In an old mother plant which has passed the blooming stage will usually be found some very potent "tea" which you would call putrid especially if you attempted to drink it. This is generally caused by the actual breaking down of the leaf and flower structures of the old plant itself after the new basal offshoots start to form. This process, no doubt, furnishes available fertilizer for the roots of the new tender offshoots formed on the side of the old plant.

There is considerable discussion regarding the watering of bromeliads in the winter time and many observations must be made of local conditions to settle

TEMPERATURE

As a family bromeliads are mostly tropical and subtropical, enduring temperatures ranging from 130° F. to the danger point of 32° F. although a few of the Tillandsias and the high Andean Puya (*Fosteriana*), which may be covered with snow at times, can endure temperatures several degrees below freezing without fatal results. *T. usneoides* can endure a temperature to near zero F.

In horticulture, with few exceptions, the well known bromeliads should not be subjected to temperatures reaching the danger point of 32° F.

The exceptions, of course, would be mostly the xerophytic and terrestrial types such as Puyas, Dyckias, Hechtias and some of the Tillandsias which are native to the colder subtropical zones. Generally speaking, the harder and stiffer the plant, the more adaptability it has to temperature or exposure. Most of the bromeliads enjoy rather cool nights in the 50's F. even those that are living at lower altitudes in warm areas.

Concerning outdoor gardens and parks where bromeliads have been used within the temperate zones not too much data is available, but in Florida and in California where on rare occasions the temperatures may reach to the low 20's F., quite a number of bromeliads have survived. Most of these, probably, have been near the ground and close to or under trees, near buildings, and in somewhat protected areas.

So, much experimentation needs to be done and records made in order to know just how much cold some of the bromeliads will stand. Quite a number of bromeliads, like *Aechmea bracteata, Ae. distichantha, Neoregelia spectabilis, N. marmorata, Tillandsia grandis, T. fasciculata, T. tricolor* and a number of the Tillandsias which are native to the United States and many parts of Mexico may stand several hours of below freezing temperatures. Strangely, I have taken ice out of plants of *Neoregelia spectabilis*, even though the species is native to frost-free, approximately sea-level altitudes in the region around Rio de Janeiro, Brazil. Their resistance is amazing, as one would hardly expect frost resistance from plants of such tropical areas; none of the Neoregelias are native to areas subject to frost.

For protection against the cold in the outside garden, throw a light covering of paper, cloth, or preferably, corrugated sheets of paper or boxes over the plants. These coverings assist in keeping the plants in closer touch with the heat of the ground and warding off the destructive frost crystals which might form upon them. This frost is destructive to almost any tender foliage even though the same plant may not be injured if the temperature should reach two to six degrees lower, provided these plants are covered or are growing under other foliage.

On the nights when a predicted frost or freeze is to occur, the bromeliads like Neoregelias and Aechmeas which might be holding a liberal amount of water in their cups would be less subject to freezing injury if these plants were lifted and emptied for that period of the freezing night and then covered with paper or cloth.

Billbergia pyramidalis, a plant which holds much water in its leaf cups, grows profusely in gardens throughout Central Florida where frosts do occur, but rarely does it have frost injury. Fortunately, it is nearly always grown under or near trees, which position affords protection. *Billbergia nutans,* as common in California gardens as is *Billbergia pyramidalis* in Florida gardens, has possibly the greatest resistance to cold of any of the Billbergias. It grows natively in temperate zone areas in Brazil, Uruguay, and Argentina, and withstands cold winters where temperatures may go down to the 20's F. on certain occasions.

Almost none of the bromeliads would show any cold injury when grown under glass if the winter temperatures do not go below 35° F.; and certainly very few greenhouses, no matter what plants are grown in them, are allowed to go to that temperature. Many of the orchids grown today would suffer from these lower temperatures, especially if they were in flower sheath or bud, much more than bromels would. A given plant may withstand more cold in a dry atmosphere than it could resist in a moist one.

Ananas   Cryptanthus   Aechmea

GROWING BROMELIADS FROM SEED

Growing bromeliads from seeds can be very interesting although there may be some disappointments ahead for the growers whether amateur or professional. The time element required has discouraged a great many horticulturists and for this reason there are still very few enthusiasts that have or will take the necessary time to grow these beautiful plants on a large scale from seed.

The fruits of most of the species which are berry-like will ripen in two to three months. As different species may vary in their time of maturity it is best to watch the fruit develop because birds, mice or roaches might take a liking to them if you are not on the alert. Many of them will turn darker and softer at maturity and should be removed as soon as ripe.

Cryptanthus fruits, especially, should be watched. The fruits are very soft when ripe, and this final ripening process may happen over night; the seeds could disappear almost as quickly, although occasionally some of them may lodge down in the leaf axils and germinate there.

When seeds are gathered from the berry-like fruits of the Bromelioideae, the seeds should be carefully cleaned, dried and then treated with Chinosol or other good disinfectant; then placed in envelopes or small containers until used. Seeds of bromeliads may retain their viability for several months, rarely more than six months, but for the best results they should be planted as soon as possible. Results are best if they are not more than three months of age.

Cleaning the seeds of a baccate fruit is a very important process, as all of the pulp from around the seeds should be removed so that decay will not soon destroy the tiny embryo in the seed. The fruits can be mashed under the forefinger or thumb on clean, absorbent paper toweling and the mess spread thin around on the paper. Once squeezed out from the fruits, the seeds should be carefully scraped off onto a new sheet of paper allowing as much of the pulp to remain on the old paper as possible. This process may be repeated, allowing the seeds to stand thus overnight to dry up the last traces of the pulp. The seeds are then ready for a soaking in a Chinosol solution for a few moments (one part to one thousandth) for sterilization to prevent growth of fungus.

The bed for seeds of the Bromelioideae, and this includes all the seeds that are without any appendage such as wings or silken threads, can be made of a mixture of one part good clean builder's sand, one half part crushed granite, and one and one-half parts of fresh German peat. Mix well and place in trays or pans with layer of broken crocks on bottom; trays should have drainage holes in bottom. Seed bed material should never be used more than once. Water down the seed bed carefully, then sprinkle seed on top. A very light sprinkling of pure sand may be sifted on the seed bed as soon as planted, but not enough to cover the seeds except those of Cryptanthus which can be just barely covered. Spray water with hand syringe and place a piece of glass an inch above the seed bed. Over this glass place a white sheet of paper for first few days until seeds have started to sprout. Seeded trays or pans should not be in sun. It is best if you can supply heat from below the seed bed keeping it at 70° to 80° F. if the weather is cool. This will not be necessary if surrounding temperature is above 75° F. Germination should take place in seven to twenty days.

If seeds are well formed, germination should be high. Some species of bromeliads will set fruits with the seeds thin or undeveloped and completely sterile, but as a rule when the fruit is fully developed the seeds are good.

Do not let the seed bed dry out or become soggy wet. Sprinkle lightly whenever necessary. Very small quantities of Fermate, to prevent damp-off can be

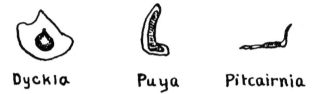

Dyckia   Puya   Pitcairnia

added to water used for sprinkling. Good clean rain water is best. Watch seedlings daily. Do not allow them to dry out or become wet; some air circulation is always necessary.

After seedlings are a half inch high a good soluble fertilizer such as Hyponex may be used. One teaspoonful added to one gallon of water is sufficient. This may be used once a week.

When seedlings are one inch high or are becoming crowded, they can be then transplanted to community pots. Twenty-five or thirty may be placed in each pot according to size. When community pots become crowded, plants can be transferred to individual two inch or two and one-half inch pots. Planting medium for community or individual pots may be same as Potting Mixture No. 1 with half the amount of fertilizer specified. Seedlings should be grown in light shade but not direct sunlight exposure.

The seeds of the subfamily Pitcairnioideae are small and dry and usually have some kind of appendage on them. They are windblown from dry pods and do not require cleaning when removed from the seed pods. They may be sown on the same seed bed material as for the members of Bromelioideae such as Aechmea, Neoregelia, Cryptanthus, etc., so the same care and instructions as for those species should be followed. Most of the dry-seed bromeliads produce very small seedlings especially Pitcairnias and much care should be used so that they will not be over-watered which may cause damp-off. Care should be used in sowing seeds rather sparsely so that they do not crowd each other in the seed bed.

The seeds of the Tillandsioideae in the genera Vriesia, Tillandsia, and Guzmania present the greatest problems. First, it takes one year from the time of flowering of the mature parent plants to ripen their seeds although there are exceptions like V. *splendens* which may mature its seed in six months. Watch the seed capsules carefully as they may suddenly open and the seeds may be blown away and lost. The seeds should be sown as fresh as possible.

The seedlings of these genera require several more years to reach maturity than do most of the species belonging to the other genera of the family. These seeds are all very small, delicate plumose seeds borne on little silken parachutes. They are dry when the fruits are ripe and have burst open. These seeds need no cleaning as there is no pulp surrounding them.

They are so delicate to handle that few growers in this country have successfully grown many of the different species; most of them have been grown in Europe where a great deal of hybridization of Vriesias and Guzmanias was carried on, especially before the World War II period. As it takes from five to eight years to mature plants from seed of Guzmania and Vriesia, there has been very little done with them in the U.S.A. Tillandsia species are for the most part still slower. Such species as *T. streptophylla* takes from eight to twelve years to mature. *T. grandis* may take from fifteen to thirty years.

Commercially, *Vriesia splendens* has been raised for many years in Europe quite successfully, but as it takes five to eight years to mature this plant it is rather expensive. And it must necessarily be so, as this is one of a number of species of Vriesias which very rarely produces additional offshoots—just one after each flowering period so there is no increase in number of plants.

There seems to be no record of any of the Tillandsia species having been grown in commercial quantities by seeds either in Europe or the United States.

The seed bed for these small seeds of Vriesias, Guzmanias and Tillandsias should be made of materials that will not break down quickly. German peat with finely crushed granite and light layer of fresh cut green sphagnum can be used. Be careful not to use old sphagnum or moss of any kind. Fern peat blocks may also be used. It is most necessary, however, that humid air conditions be retained. Especially is it necessary to keep evenly balanced moist conditions; small seedlings must not be allowed to dry off. More shade is necessary than with the seedlings of the other two subfamilies. Your most careful attention must be given during the first three months in the early germinating and developing periods. Glass covers should be used to assist in regulating moisture.

While in the United States today we are growing far more decorative house plants of all kinds than have ever been grown in any other country, in Belgium, however, there are a greater number of bromeliads being grown commercially today than were ever grown in the United States at any time. The principal species grown there and in other European countries is *Aechmea fasciata,* as well as some of the Neoregelia hybrids. This *A. fasciata* species has been grown in Europe from seed for more than a half century and it still remains one of the favorite house plants in Europe. Why not grow more bromeliads in the United States from seed?

Guzmania   Vriesia

NOTES ON GROWING FROM SEED

Charles Webb

When growing bromeliads from seed it is the writer's firm conviction, based on experiments over nearly three years, that the most essential ingredients to success are as follows and in the order given.

The seed must be as fresh as possible.

The atmosphere must be damp but bouyant.

The temparature must be sufficient to germinate but not excessively hot and should be free as possible from fluctuation.

The compost must be open, sweet, and be in sufficient quantity to insure that frequent waterings are not necessary.

Once the seed has sprouted and is large enough to handle, it should be pricked out into community pans. (Shallow pans are less liable to "go sour" than pots) and receive more open air to harden them off and thus prevent damp-off.

This period of transition is fraught with danger but is blessed if kept in the same atmosphere as the younger plants for a short while to recover from the shock.

As regards temperature the writer's experience showed if undue heat was used damp-off seemed inevitable and the survivors were weaklings.

Various plants require different temperatures but the writer's experiments on that score are incomplete.

In regards to compost, seeds will germinate on almost anything, but the subsequent requirements differ considerably. The standard compost now used by the writer is approximately:

¼ good loam
¼ peat
¼ old leaf-mold
¼ coarse sand

Once the seed has germinated and the seedlings are about to form their root systems, they are pricked off into community pans but varying the soil to suit.

Puyas and other sun lovers more sand and less peat is used.

Neoregelias and Aechmeas less loam is used. Vriesias also get less loam but extra sand.

As far as mature plants are concerned the writer is now convinced that the cardinal sin is too much water.

13 Elizabeth Ave., Dulwich Hill, Sydney, N.S.W., Australia

STORAGE OF AECHMEA SEED

JOSEPH CARRONE, JR.

EVERYONE KNOWS that seeds of Aechmeas and many other bromeliads as well lose vigor, germinate slower, etc., when dried for storage. As in the case with many complicated hybrids, only comparatively fresh seeds will germinate. This has been the case with us and others as well.

Hybrids two or more generations removed from the species must be planted almost immediately upon harvesting for them to grow. In short, hybrid vigor does not extend beyond the F1 generation. Subsequent hybridization is thwarted by a degree of sterility at the chromosonal level with the result that viable seeds are not produced. Those few that do form seem very temperamental, especially at the start. To subject such seeds to a drying period, if a delay in sowing them is necessary, is sure to mean failure. Perhaps this article will make possible - maybe only one time - the success in germinating some fine thing that would otherwise not result because of poor storage methods before the seeds are sown. Who knows how far such a method of storage of seed will go. We can't now tell!

Many of our bromeliads grow outside under Maxlite plastic panels with a heavy wire fabric forming a back drop on which we hang Platycerium ferns and hundreds of bromeliads on cork and tree fern plaques and other suitable materials. This area, as you can visualize, is open and to some extent unprotected from ravenous birds, squirrels and the like that may feast on some eagerly awaited seed capsule. For this reason when a number of such capsules were noticed turning bluish, I gathered them and cleaned the seeds of all pulp as outlined in a previous article of mine in the *Bulletin*.

Because I had no time to sow the seeds immediately, as I much prefer to do, I placed them in a small vial with a quanity of clear tap water, capped the bottle, and put it on my desk until later.

When two days had gone by and still I had not found time to sow the seeds, rather than subject them to drying for storage, I decided to rinse them well once again, re-place a like quality of water in the vial with them, and let them go a while longer. At this point, however, I became concerned about the probability of their beginning to grow while still in the water; the temperature was well up into the eighties and with moisture and warmth germination was likely. This would have brought about the loss of many seeds. Well, do you know what I did? Yes, I placed the vial of seeds and water in the refrigerator. I know that they would not be frozen; they were not placed too near the freezer compartment. Here the lower temperature would surely retard germination until I wanted them to grow.

Nearly a month went by and I had forgotten all about the seeds until Susan, my wife, reminded me that they were still in the refrigerator. Well, like a bolt of lightning, I recovered the vial with its precious contents and noted that through all this time there was no apparent change in the seeds. I sowed them. In less than a week the plaques were covered with Aechmea seedlings just as though they had sprung from freshly collected seeds — germination was quite satisfactory!

Perhaps I was just lucky, but this goes to show that storage of Aechmea seeds is possible in the fresh (not dried) state. — *New Orleans, Louisiana.*

POLLINATION

Excerpt from Walter Richter's -
Bromeliad Handbook
"Anzucht und Kultur der Bromeliaceen"
translated from the German by Joseph Schneider

Nature has many varied ways to effect pollination. Nectar-secreting organs, intensive colored bracts, attract insects and birds, a part of the inflorescence undoubtedly takes part in attracting pollinizers. *Vriesia splendens, Guzmania monostachys, Billbergia rosea* and others are self-fertile. Perhaps this compensates for the infrequency of off-sets these plants produce. Seeds of these plants germinate quickly, and easily. In this manner does Nature often insure continuity of the species. Self-sterility is frequent and is an important factor for the practical grower. To insure production of seed at least two specimens of about the same state of development are necessary, a condition often difficult to meet with rarer species, making seed production impossible. The time available to effect pollination is often very short; flowers open often only a few hours, or up to two days. These short-lasting flowers may further limit the opportunity for pollination, opening only nights, or late afternoon, and fade quickly. Some Vriesia species, for instance, *Vriesia tesselata, V. fenestralis,* and others, open nights only, others in the early morning hours, to close again at sunrise. The length of time the flowers remain open, depends, probably, a great deal upon temperature. Individual florets of winter-flowering Vriesias remain open about two days, while summer-flowering species do so only a single day. For the normal growth of the pollen, temperature, as well as humidity, has to be right. Pollination in winter, with the lower temperatures prevailing, is nearly always a failure. In nature, butterflies, bumblebees, bees and other small insects, the humming-birds, especially, serve as pollinizers. The nectar-gathering species, with their long, sharp bills, can enter flowers that remain, normally, closed. Ants play often an important role as pollenizers. I observed how a very small species of ant that somehow had found entrance into the glass-house effected the pollinization of an Aechmea species that I was never able to pollinize successfully. On the other hand, if ants gain access to flowers, normally remaining closed, that had been cut open to pollinize, they quickly chew off the stigma and pistils, and do considerable damage. To get *Tillandsia lindenii*, with its varieties *vera* and *tricolor* to set seed is very difficult. One must visualize that the seed-producing organs of these beautiful flowers are one inch deep in a long narrow duct that is strongly compressed by the tightly imbricated sepals of the inflorescence. The thinking grower cannot help wondering and being intrigued and puzzled again and again what secrets this tropical plant world conceals. Bromels, are aptly called "Bird-flowers", flower and bird, both combine to convey tropical beauty and unique charm.

Crimmitschau, Germany

Aechmea fasciata

Canistrum fosterianum

Billbergia venezuelana

Photo Courtesy Oakhurst Gardens

Removing offshoot from mature plant

PROPAGATION BY OFFSHOOT

The propagation of most bromeliads can be carried out in two ways: by offsets (asexually) and by seeds (sexually).

A majority of the species of this great family would continue to live on indefinitely by developing and maturing the offshoots they produce after each flowering period unless they met with some external catastrophe. This asexual growth serves them well, but in the case of the epiphytic species which are not stoloniferous and live in the trees, it becomes their nemesis because they often develop clusters so large that they fall to their doom of their own weight. The sexual development by seed, therefore, must always be present for their survival in all the species.

The horticulturist has then, in most instances, two methods that he may use for the propagation of these plants.

Many species of Aechmeas and Neoregelias will produce as many as six to twelve offshoots from one plant if they are removed as soon as each one reaches a size having a number of leaves and a firm or hard base or stolon. There is a possible eye at the base of each leaf that could develop into a side shoot, but this rarely, if ever, occurs except possibly in the Cryptanthus species.

To propagate bromeliads in large commercial quantities to be sold at reasonable prices, they will, in most species, have to be raised by seed. The reason, of course, is obvious, as the space necessary for any great production of plants from offshoots would be very costly unless the grower is located in a section where the plants could be grown in beds where frost is not a hazard and space is ample and inexpensive. Again, the Cryptanthus species is one of the few exceptions. The plants are small and generally have very few seeds but many offshoots.

Some bromeliads produce a number of offshoots as soon as the plant has flowered, as in most of the Cryptanthus species. These plants, however, will produce a greater number of offshoots if they are removed as soon as they have reached a size large enough for them to withstand the shock of removal from the parent. These offshoots should be removed without the aid of a knife or instrument, just pulled off with a pressure from side to side; if left on for some time they may fall off when struck accidentally. I have taken as many as twenty offshoots from one Cryptanthus plant over a period of twelve to twenty months. Nearly all of the bromeliad species in cultivation will produce more than one offshoot, but if the first offshoots are not removed when they reach approximately one-fourth to one-sixteenth of the height of the parent plant, this mature plant in many species will develop only one or two offshoots and gradually the old leaves will die off one by one. If none of the shoots are removed the plant will gradually develop into a cluster of two or more heads and thus increase in size after each annual flowering period. *Billbergia nutans*, for example, may fill a tub over a period of years and make a grand specimen.

While there are but a few species of bromeliads in horticulture that do not produce offshoots, there are a number of hybrids that can only be reproduced by offshoots because the flowers are sterile and will produce no seed.

Then, too, there are certain hybrids that will occasionally set seed when pollinated but the offspring would be most variable. Thus certain named hybrids would have to be reproduced by offshoots entirely unless a cross using the same parents could be repeated as often as desired. This, of course, is not always possible unless the grower has a liberal number of both parent plants and they both flower at the same time each year.

It is not difficult to remove the offshoots from the parent plant for propagation but care should be used in this operation. Plants like *Aechmea miniata var. discolor, A. fulgens, A. Racinae, Nidularium amazonicum, Quesnelia liboniana* and many others that produce the offshoots on rather hard stems or stolons are easily handled. Generally, the offshoots can be broken off by hand if the stolon is held firmly near the point of attachment to the parent plant. These stolons can also be cut off from the parent with a sharp knife. Many Neoregelias also can be taken by hand when one learns the technique of detaching, but if one is not sure, then the knife should be used.

When the offshoots are pulled off, practically all of these suckers can be potted at once if desired. As there is no cambium layer to cause a callus as in the dicotyledons, there need be no trimming at base unless the stolon is too long for potting. It is best that the base be rather hard and woody, because it is possible for the offshoot to rot back if it is too young and succulent or if it is cut too closely to the crown of the leaves.

Tubular plants of Billbergias and other genera often have fewer offshoots, no doubt, because most of these species of this shape have fewer leaves than the open rosette type of plants.

112

Aechmea fasciata, A. marmorata, Billbergia saundersii and other similar growth plants usually develop their suckers on rather thick, succulent stolons; these should be severed with a knife at a point close to the parent plant. Most of the Neoregelias, on the other hand, produce their offshoots rather close with little development of a stolon. These are easily removed by cutting as close as possible to the parent plant.

Dyckias have two types of offsets. Many of them can be reproduced by offsets developed on stolons as *D. leptostachys;* others by separation of double and triple heads which are gradually formed as in *D. Fosteriana* and *D. sulphurea,* but *D. frigida* continues for many years to grow without producing offsets or by subdivision of the rosette, thus producing a long prostrate caudex or trunk. Therefore reproduction is in this type made only by seeds.

Some of the Vriesia species such as *V. splendens* do not produce offsets from the side of the plant, and they can be reproduced only by seeds. There are several Vriesias in this class with *V. splendens* which instead of producing side shoots produce a new growth just off center within the rosette next to the inflorescence. As this new center develops, the old mature leaves gradually die off and in the course of nine to twelve months the old leaves have entirely gone while the new fully developed plant, which has gradually produced new roots, has entirely replaced the old plant. This performance will continue on for years after each flowering but there will not be, except in rare instances, any more plants than the original seedling started with.

How long does it take to mature a bromeliad? A few species of bromeliads will mature to flowering stage from seed in two to three years, principally some of the Billbergias and a few of the Aechmeas. Neoregelias and most Aechmeas take longer, from three to four years; Vriesias from five to seven years. Tillandsias from five to thirty years; Dyckias two to five years; Cryptanthus, two to three years.

Offshoots, of course, will reach flowering maturity in most species sooner than the seedlings would. Most of the species in Billbergias may bloom in the following years. Aechmeas and Neoregelias from one to two years; Vriesias from one to two years; Cryptanthus, one year, some exceptions in two or three years. However, this condition depends somewhat as to whether an offshoot is removed when very small or fairly well developed.

There are a number of species of bromeliads such as *Tillandsia utriculata, T. grandis, Puya raimondii* and others that do not produce any offshoots after flowering. They flower but once, disperse their seeds and die. *Puya raimondii* never produces any side shoots but *Tillandsia grandis* produces numerous small seedling-like plants at the base while still in an immature stage—for the first five to ten years, but none later as the plant grows to maturity in twenty to thirty years.

THE PROGRESSIVE CARE OF SEEDLINGS

Walter Richter

(From *Anzucht und Kultur des Bromeliaceen* published in Germany, 1950)

Too early transplanting of seedlings is detrimental and they should be kept in their original pan until too crowded. In about four to six months after sowing, they will want more room and then can be transplanted into pans filled with heath-soil. Seedlings are delicate and must be handled gently. Add some rubbed or chopped sphagnum moss or rubbed peat moss into the soil if the plants are large enough. They should be kept in the warm house and temperature should not be below 68 to 70°. They grow much better in a high temperature. If moss and algae get into the seed pan, transplant them into fresh material. As plants gain strength, the soil mixture should be made coarser to keep the soil well drained.

When the seedling plants look as if they might do better with more room, there are two things you can do. If you have only a few plants, put them into pots, always using the smallest pot that will accommodate them — later, too, use small pots. The small root system of the various species cannot make use of large pots. As a general guide, repotting once a year is sufficient. A tight ball is an advantage. Why? you might ask. The roots of Bromels are primarily hold-fast organs and their use as water and nutrient absorbing organs is secondary. A well-felted ball is not detrimental as it can be with other plants; on the contrary, these plants seem to thrive especially well. Always pot tight. Your potting material is continually breaking down and decomposing and plants tend to get loose.

If a large quantity of plants is to be handled, it is best to transplant them into raised beds in benches. The benches can be of concrete but must provide adequate drainage. Wood does not last long under the necessary wet conditions. Ground beds are not well suited; they are hard to heat and bottom heat is of great advantage. Beds must not be deeper than five or six inches. Have a one-inch layer of coarse peat or potsherds for good drainage. The soil mixture can be fairly coarse — heath-soil, peat, half-rotted leaves, sphagnum and sand. The whole should be spongy and porous. The same mixture can be used for potting. Coarse leaf mold is good for the more terrestrial species like Aechmeas. Avoid using too much for Nidulariums, however, as this species does not like the impermeable, sticky mess that broken-down leaf-mold soon forms. Pound some old pots into small pieces and mix with leaf-mold. Bromels like to get their roots around them and hold onto. Try to keep the soil acid — 4-4.5 pH.

When planting out into benches, set the plants far enough apart to allow at least a season's growth and do not plant too deep; if planted too shallow, however, they may lean or topple over. They like to sit solid in loose material, so compact the soil well around them when setting out. Plants do definitely better when planted out in benches and it is easier to water them. Soak dry spots once a week with a sprinkling can; for general watering go over them with a hose. Proper humidity has to be maintained at all times.

By the third year most of the plants will have reached considerable size, depending upon the species. Aechmeas, Neoregelias, Billbergias, and Nidulariums grow much faster than Guzmanias and Vriesias. From here on they need different treatment; the last-mentioned slow growers should stay in the warm house with high temperatures, plenty of shade, and correspondingly high humidity. For best results, if space permits, they could be transplanted again to good advantage, replant them so that the outer leaf-tips barely touch. For species that need less heat — Aechmeas, Neoregelias, Billbergias, Nidulariums, and such — frames can be utilized from May to September; if they can be heated, so much the better. Use frames in good condition, running north and south.

Some Vriesias and Vriesia hybrids can be set out in frames also when they are about three years old. But *Vriesia hieroglyphica* and the various forms of *Vriesia splendens* and its hybrids must be kept in a warm house. *Vriesia splendens* comes from Guiana, near the equator, and wants warmth and humidity to do well. The majority of the green-leaved Vriesias come from the mountainous part of Brazil, and the conditions a frame provides suits them well. As can be seen, it is of practical advantage to learn about the natural habitat of these plants.

When setting plants out into frames, they should not be placed in beds but rather kept in their pots. Spread a layer of some water-absorbing material into the frame, set the pots on this, and spray as needed to keep up the humidity. For shade use cloth rather than boards. Keep frames closed. When the weather starts to get hot, however, open the frames during the hottest part of the day, but close in time to give the sun a chance to warm up the frame for the night and see that the plants are dry for the night hours. Towards September get the plants used to more light by taking off some of the shading, being careful not to burn them — this might easily happen on a hot sunny day. To get approximately the same light duration (12 hours) they enjoy in their natural home, it is best to shade the houses in summer; the plants do better and the difference between day and night temperatures is less sharp. Towards the end of September it will be necessary to take the plants out of the frames and to bring them into a light, sunny and fairly warm greenhouse. To make full use of available space, the plants can be tiered.

Facilities for provision of bottom heat are a great advantage, though not absolutely necessary. To prevent too much loss of heat by draughts from below, the benches can be covered by coke screenings; during summer a cover of peat is better as it helps to provide humidity.

At the beginning of, or during the third or fourth year, most of the seedlings will begin to flower. Until the plants show bud they can well be left in their small propagating pots without harm, and later, when they are ready to flower, planted into display pots.

All that has been said about seedlings applies as well to the vegetatively raised plants.

Crimmitschau-Sachsen, D. D. R.

BROMELIADS CAN MAKE A TREE GARDEN
Racine Foster

Those of us who are lucky enough to live in the subtropical climes can have the pleasure of a tree garden as an attractive, carefree feature to the garden area. A tree garden in the tropical jungle includes orchids, rhipsalis, bromeliads and a host of other epiphytes; in making our own, here in Florida, we neglected all the plant families except the bromeliads! So, we have our palms full of Aechmeas, Billbergias and Tillandsias.

It is the "boots" of the Phoenix or Sabal palms that make such favorable starting places for bromeliads. This pocket holds the bromeliad upright while it is getting established in the mass of natural residue of decayed matter also held by the "boot."

Other than an occasional watering we forget them (except when visitors rave over them) and they take clouds or sun, drouth or rain, hurricanes and cold weather, just as it comes without a protest. Once established the Aechmeas put out hard stolons that cling to the palm and form an encircling procession, in time, around the trunk continuing their upward climb, apparently happy for they have increased abundantly and bloom vigorously every year.

The rough bark of oak trees also serves very well for establishing a tree garden; the plants can be attached with string or covered wire at first but as soon as the new offshoots have put out roots you can forget them, for, from here they will be on their own without artificial support. Particles of leaves and debris, with now and then a bit of fertilizer from the birds, will drop into the cups of the leaves thus completing the rations for good bromeliad health.

BROMELIADS AS A PART OF CALIFORNIA LANDSCAPE DESIGN

Victoria Padilla

Although California is the only state bordering the south where bromeliads are not found growing natively, there are probably, with the exception of Florida, more bromeliads to be found under cultivation in the area south of Santa Barbara than in any other section of the United States. This is rather odd when one considers the adverse conditions under which these plants must grow.

The climate of Southern California is similar to that found in the Mediterranean region—long, dry summers and cool, moist winters, just the type of weather which most bromeliads do not like. But such a situation merely presents a challenge to the intrepid California gardener—and come drought or flood, freezing or scorching weather, he is always willing to try his hand in taming the wild or adapting the exotic to his desert-like conditions.

Bromeliads are to be found more and more as a part of the landscape design in Southern California, and strangely enough, they are responding to the many peculiar situations under which they are finding themselves.

Billbergias are the most commonly grown bromeliads in Southern California and are seen everywhere. They are used successfully bordering the shady walk, filling in a dark spot where nothing else will grow, acting as a relief alongside begonias and fuchsias in the sheltered garden, hanging gracefully from hanging baskets, or drooping reflectively over the edge of a pool.

The large Aechmeas, *Ae. caudata variegata, Ae. distichantha,* and *Ae. bracteata* are being grown as accent notes where a tropical effect is desired. Large clumps of *Ae. distichanta* are effective when used to break up expanses of lawn, the leaves giving that often desired perpendicular effect. Instead of New Zealand Flax (*Phormium tenax*) *Ae. caudata variegata* is found to be equally imposing (and more so when in flower) placed on either side of a doorway. *Ae. bracteata* is often seen growing with aralias, palms, philodendrons, and bamboo in plantings against a modern house.

In the coastal sections where frosts occur but seldom, many of the less hardy aechmeas, such as *Ae. Weilbachii, Ae. fasciata, Ae. pineliana,* and *Ae. miniata* are being planted in the open in rockeries. The author has a rock garden devoted exclusively to bromeliads—Aechmeas, Billbergias, Quesnelias, Nidulariums, and Neoregelias—the odd red, purple, and orange tones of the volcanic rock proving to be a striking foil for the colorful plants. Planted in partial shade, in half leaf mold and half sand, being given excellent drainage, the bromelaids are perfectly happy. The only problem will be to keep them within bounds.

In plantings under large trees, landscape architects are tending to use more bromeliads grown in among ferns, Cymbidiums, Camellias, and other semi-shade lovers. And on the trees themselves, along side of Laelias, Epidendrums, and other hardy orchids, Aechmeas, Tillandsias, and Billbergias are being successfully grown. In the Oakhurst Gardens in Arcadia, where it often hits freezing during the winter months, bromeliads of many varieties are to be seen growing on the limbs of old, gigantic oaks—continuously blooming and increasing in size.

As many Southern Californians are patio dwellers, much attention is being paid to making this living area as attractive as possible. Usually the effect desired is a tropical one, and bromeliads are used to help attain this feeling of lush, jungle growth. In one planting in the patio of a large department store, plants of *Billbergia porteana,* always large and striking, add a definite note of interest in among the palms and philodendrons. In patios, bromeliads grow successfully in open planters, in pots, in hanging baskets, in fernwood containers, or attached to bits of driftwood, a form of decoration currently very popular in this part of the world. Some of the healthiest bromeliads this author has seen are growing in the patio of a friend who resides in one of the driest and warmest parts of the Southland, two thousand feet above the San Fernando valley.

Although Southern Californians are doing their best to make their section of the state a sub-tropical paradise, Southern California remains nevertheless a semi-desert region. (The rainfall for 1952-53 being eight inches). Thus more and more gardeners, unable to cope with the excessive alkalinity of the Colorado river water which they must use, are growing those plants which require little moisture—succulents and cacti. One of the most famous gardens of this kind to be found anywhere is located in the Huntington Botanical Gardens in San Marino. Outstanding in this garden is the collection of bromeliads—Puyas, Hectias, Dyckias, and the like—which when in bloom attract visitors from near and far. This planting has done much to encourage the growing of terrestrial bromeliads in home gardens. There are many excellent specimens of *Puya alpestris* to be seen in private estates, and this bromeliad has become so popular that it can be purchased in any of the larger nurseries.

So in the open or under shelter, in the sun or in the shade, under trees or clinging to their branches, bromeliads are now to be found in California gardens—a permanent part of their landscape design.

Everyone who starts a collection of plants goes through a period of endeavoring to keep an accurate record of his plants as to when they were purchased, size, price, etc. As the collection grows, such bookkeeping tends to become a laborious task and in most times given up completely. Actually, all that is needed is a good label system. Get a label that is large enough to start with, so that you can note on it the date of bloom and the date of repotting. Use a number to designate offshoots, such as, *Aechmea fasciata* 1, 2, or 3. Colored labels can be used to differentiate between genera or be put on a plant that is available for trading.

NEW STYLES IN BROMELIAD TREES

David Barry, Jr.

Bromeliads make an ideal medium for interior plant arrangements. The color and symmetry of their shapely rosettes; the style and variety of their form and silhouette challenge the imagination of both plant grower and artist. Clever and graceful arrangements have been made of bromeliads placed on branches and trees, on bark or cork-covered metal pipes that resemble trees, and on assemblies of bark and cork slabs. Illustrations and descriptions of such artistic work with bromeliads have appeared from time to time in the "Bulletin", and have further stimulated efforts to combine the beauty and the usefulness of these plants in outstanding interior arrangements. The term applied to such collections of bromeliads mounted on dead branches, regardless of size, is "Bromeliad Tree."

The prototypes were very large tree-like branches, or sometimes entire trees, that were decorated with bromeliads and served as displays in flower shows, conservatories, or good-sized interior planting areas and alcoves. Large branches were firmly placed in the ground, and, when effectively decorated with bromeliads, these "trees" became focal points of interest. (Incidentally, because of the epiphytic nature of the plants, they were frequently mistaken for orchids, especially when in spike, and were often called parasites.) Beautiful as these large trees were, however, the typical bromeliad grower could not be their proud possessor. They took up too much space, and watering the numerous plants was no small problem. With these limitations in mind, we experimented with smaller trees, and, in doing so, developed an assortment of new forms that still retained the designation: bromeliad tree.

The smaller bromeliad trees are most useful and practical as house plants. Their beauty and novelty "steal the show." Watering is no longer a major problem, for these light trees can be taken with ease to the kitchen sink or laundry tray, where the moss balls about the roots can be saturated and the rosettes filled. The trees are then left to drip-dry before being returned to their place of honor.

However, have nothing to do with these bromeliad trees unless you love both artistry and bromeliads, for you must be willing to go through the watering routine every two or three days. The extent to which you will be rewarded for this form of slavery is in your heart and soul, and also in your ears, unless you remain deaf to the audible admiration of your friends.

When we began to develop these smaller "trees", we erred in two ways. First, we impatiently struck them in plaster of paris to anchor them in containers, only to discover that plaster of paris disintegrated with moisture. We should have used a concrete mixture, and waited until the next day to affix the plants. Second, we were not selective enough either as to the shape of the driftwood or as to its relationship with the container. We had to learn to use critical judgment and to adhere to the rules of design in order to achieve an art form of balanced asymmetry with the driftwood and its container - a combination giving a pleasing effect even without plants. Then, with the addition of the plants, we had a creation that truly delighted the eye.

The arrangement of the plants became a study. We used mostly odd, and not even, numbers of plants. Beginning with the lowest bromeliad planted in the container, we sought to place them so as to form an ascending design in a curve or curves. Also, the plants were sized, the largest at the bottom to give the base weight. This effect is also attained by arrangement, the darker the foliage, the lower the plant. How arty can one get!

In some bromeliad trees we used but one species, all the same size, such as *Vriesia carinata.* A few months after one such tree was made all of the plants spiked at once. The pleasure to be gained from this form is like that derived from repetition of a pattern in formal wallpaper or in certain fabrics. It makes an interesting contrast to the tree on which variations in color and shape are used.

Our latest development is the most sophisticated - painting the driftwood a color that is related to the color of the bromeliads. The effect is that of a living mural. The combination of the live plants on wood shaped by nature, yet colored artificially is surprising and pleasing and of course the color must be the right color. When we painted the wood the exact shade of rich, dark brown as that of the barring on *Vriesia splendens,* it was immediately evident that we had chosen the right color. Then

Placing the large plant at the base gives stability to the arrangement

we grew bolder and painted one tree a dusty rose to serve as a foil for the pink in the leaves of plants such as *Nididularium kermesiana.* The painting of the wood can also be a dulled background for the brighter foliage of the plants. Keep this kind of bromeliad tree away from other plants, say, in front of a monotone background.

Practical observations:

1. Form a plant pocket in the cement that holds the tree in the container.

2. Affix the bromeliads *tightly* to the branch by forming a sphagnum moss ball about the roots, and then wiring on the ball of moss by winding the wire first around a small part or tack, and then pulling portions of the moss between the wires in order to hide the wires. Use a pinch of leaf mold with the moss, if you desire, but we have not found this to be necessary.

3. Soak the moss occasionally with a dilute fertilizer when watering.

4. Unless the plants are allowed to suffer from lack of water, you will not find it difficult to maintain the plants in good health on the trees. We have kept them happily installed for several plant generations.

5. Pebbles may be used to hide the cement concrete anchoring of the tree in the container.

6. As to kinds of trees, grapes, figs, driftwood, or such naturally smooth woods as manzanita are recommended.

7. An easy way to apply water to the moss is to use a basting syringe that can be found in most super markets.

8. A very small bromeliad tree may be made with a height above the rim of the container of about eighteen inches, using only three plants, the largest being planted in the container.

9. We gave up the "flag pole effect", that is, placing the driftwood straight up in the center of the container. Some of the most satisfying trees were arranged with an asymmetrical, bonzai, effect.

10. We make no attempt to excavate plant pockets in the wood, for we found this unnecessary. After awhile, many of the plants developed wire-like hold-fast roots that encircle the bare wood where they are probably better off than in a hole.

HOW I PLANT EPIPHYTIC BROMELIADS ON WOOD

Richard Oeser, M.D.

When our secretary, Miss Victoria Padilla, visited me in 1956, she saw how I grow my Tillandsias, and in the May 1957 issue of the Bulletin, she wrote about them in an article entitled "Tillandsia Mobiles." I would like to add a few remarks to what she had to say and to clarify them with some pictures.

The best wood for the creation of a "Tillandsia Mobile" is an old grapevine trunk, although other bent and twisted limbs and roots can be used effectively. As these wooden pieces are seldom naturally so formed as to be just what is desired in the way of shape, I often find it necessary to take two or three pieces of wood and fasten them together with galvanized wire. Usually I place one piece upright and the other in a horizontal position. It is often advisable to fasten a second piece of wood horizontally behind the first one, so that the upright piece is clamped between the front and the rear pieces. By twisting the wire into a figure eight, I can join the wood together so that the wire is hardly noticeable.

I drill a hole at the upper end of the upright piece, and with the same wire make a hanger by looping the wire around twice, twisting it tight and bending the ends into a hook. Planting material can be inserted into any gaps formed by the joining of the pieces of wood.

To fasten the plants onto the wood I take an inch-wide strip of nylon hose, which I obtain by cutting the hose crosswise with scissors. I then wrap these elastic strips around the roots of the plants, about which has been placed an amount of planting medium (such as osmunda), and then fasten the bromeliad at a suitable place. Pincers can be used to great advantage to thread the nylon strips around the cross pieces. The knots of the nylon strips and the ends of the wire should be as inconspicuous as possible. Wood does shrink in time and the wires are apt to get lose, but rather than twisting the wire where it was originally joined as it can easily break, I shorten the wire at another place by gripping it with pliers and giving it half a twist.

In this way nearly all epiphytic bromeliads can be made into mobiles and suspended from the ceiling. They can be easily taken care of, and besides the usual spraying can be immersed when necessary in a tub of water. These mobiles can be effectively used for interior decoration, hanging near or in front of a window. Spraying or immersing can be done in the bathroom and the mobile left there to drip and then rehung in the window without soiling the room by the procedure.

I believe that there are special advantages to this method as compared to that using cork or oak bark. First, such wood pieces do not obstruct to any extent the light from the window as would the wider oak bark slab; and secondly, such wood pieces tend to let the water drain from the plants in a natural way, thus doing away with the possibility of the roots having damp feet. Also, as the plants grow, the wood does not get top heavy, tipping toward the front, but the bromeliads can grow and spread naturally, eventually covering the wood on all sides.

Kirchzarten, bei Freiburg I, Brsg. Hebelstrasse 5 Germany

BROMELIADS IN THE ROCK GARDEN
From "Bromeliads in Florida Horticulture"
Mulford B. Foster

A large number of terrestrial bromeliads are growing on or among rocks in their native haunts in Brazil, Peru, Chile, and elsewhere in the Americas. So, as introduced exotics, we have bromeliads in the genera of Dyckia, Hechtia, Encholirium, Bromelia, Neoglaziovia, Orthophytum, and Ananas which make excellent rock garden plants. These are gradually being introduced and propagated for the "new look" in rock gardens. A number of Dyckias have already been in cultivation and general distribution for a number of years, but there are many more, even more attractive, to be made known to the rock garden fancier. The other genera named are, unfortunately, very much less known but hold much interest for the courageous gardener who will risk something new. They not only have interesting and tough foliage, but brilliant spikes of flowers of endless variety and color.

Two excellent rock garden bromeliads have proved to be in the genus Neoregelia, *N. spectabilis* (Painted Fingernail) and *N. marmorata* (Marble Plant) and hybrids of these. Their leaves become very red in full sun and their wire-like roots fasten themselves eagerly on the porous rocks of either coquina or limestone. The Neoregelias are more of an epiphytic type of bromeliad but they have adapted themselves so remarkably well in our own rock garden and others of central and south Florida that now we are recommending them as a colorful, novel addition to home-made rock gardens.

Not to be forgotten are the Pitcairnias, a terrestrial leafy bromeliad which can be happy in the shaded garden either among rocks or near a pool. A number of the species remind one of tufts of grass, such as *Pitcairnia flammea*, until they produce their brilliant red tubular flowers on a branched spike which in some species continue to bloom for two months, such as *P. corallina*.

718 Magnolia Avenue, Orlando, Florida.

DECORATING WITH BROMELIADS . . .

Ellsworth

Padilla

Bromeliads fit into any kind of decorating scheme. The upper picture shows a planting at the Jos. Schlitz Brewing Company in Tampa, Florida.

The photo to the left shows Cryptbergia used in the home.